The Dark Side of Paradise

The Dark Side of Paradise

Odd and Intriguing Stories from Vero Beach

RICHARD J. KERR

RAND-SMITH PUBLISHING
VIENNA

Print ISBN: 978-1-950544-00-4

Digital ISBN: 978-1-950544-01-1

Registered with the Library of Congress

Illustrations courtesy of Andre Kerr and Enzo Kerr

Rand-Smith

Rand-Smith Publishing
www.Rand-Smith.com

Vienna, VA

Printed in the USA

Reviews

"Richard Kerr is a gold mine of storytelling waiting to be discovered in the imagination of Dick Kerr. His considerable wit and gifted insight I have known for many years in his other lives urges the reader to go on without hesitation or a break. The book is further proof of the character and Tom Sawyer-like American spirit that lives inside Dick Kerr's imagination. Read 'The Dark Side of Paradise'; you won't regret it."

Lt. General Kenneth Minihan (Ret), former head of the National Security Agency (NSA) and the Defense Intelligence Agency (DIA)

"'The Dark Side of Paradise' promises to unsheathe the mind of the reader into the bizarre and hilariously creative world of Richard Kerr. A mind that the CIA employed for 33 years in the troubled parts of the world, including briefing U.S. presidents in the White House, where through insights and analysis Kerr attempted to make meaning out of the anomalies of different people and cultures that sometimes did or attempted to do damage to the United States. Kerr's sketches and short stories remind me of the insightful and artistic talent of James Thurber."

Stanford Erickson, author, reporter and editor who covered the White House, Congress and international trade and economics

"Dick Kerr has written a number of entertaining short stories, a rarity these days, that are alternately funny, bemusing, disturbing and sometimes downright weird. Nearly all are food for thought. I thoroughly enjoyed them."

Robert M. Gates an American statesman, scholar and university president who served as Secretary of Defense, and Director of Central Intelligence

"Dick has written a delightful series of short stories and vignettes. There is a strong hint of irony in many of them, recalling the best from the old Twilight Zone series. At many places, I found myself laughing out loud — always a good sign."

Mark Lowenthal former Assistant Director of Central Intelligence for Analysis & Production, Vice Chairman of the National Intelligence Council, Staff Director of House Intelligence Committee and 1988 Jeopardy Grand Champion

"Dick Kerr gives a broad new meaning to intelligence. His quirky, humorous writings with illustrations range in subjects from murder to the absurd, leaving the reader with a jolt of laughter. The surprise endings are reminiscent of O. Henry. Kerr's writing has been honed and his mind and imagination twisted by his association with an eclectic group, the Sandfly Scribblers."

Rody Johnson comes from a long line of Vero Beach residents is an author of several books

Contents

Part III. Twilight

Part IV. Cache

Introduction

I packed a considerable amount of experiences into 33 years of service at the CIA—traveling, meeting with presidents and kings, and participating in critical national security issues. My plan for life after the agency was nonexistent, but within a few weeks of feeling cast adrift, several opportunities appeared. Boards, study groups and heading a government-industry association filled the time. I also was asked by the State Department to serve as the US member of a commission monitoring compliance with the "Good Friday" agreement that promised the end of strife in Northern Ireland. Heading a controversial study of intelligence provided to policy makers before the war with Iraq presented another real challenge.

My wife and I moved to the Outer Banks of North Carolina while I continued my work in the Washington area. Then a trip to Vero Beach to visit our daughter changed everything. We sold the house in North Carolina and settled into a quaint community in this beautiful little tropical paradise.

Shortly after moving to Vero Beach I was asked to join a writing group that had been meeting for a few years just down the street. A mother-and-daughter team had put together ten or so people who meet each Monday to read and comment on their memoirs, draft manuscripts, and short stories. The group is called the Sandfly Scribblers, named for a street in Vero.

I had been writing on foreign policy issues as a CIA analyst and manager for over 30 years and had written chapters for books on intelligence analysis as well as a short autobiography that was published in Bulgaria. I had never tried my hand at fiction.

My first efforts were several exercises suggested by a "how to write" book that the group was reading. The idea was to write a paragraph describing a café, a fruit stand, a restroom and so on. After those exercises, I began to write my own short stories. My style evolved into crisp, brief, and unencumbered prose. I tried to follow the example of several masters of the short story: Mark Twain, Gogol, Saki, Poe, Ambrose Bierce, and others. Most of mine started out several pages long and then were reduced to one or two pages. I had time to write short.

It is not clear to me exactly where the ideas for my stories come from: a dark hole in my mind, a forgotten news story, my former professional life experiences, who knows? At first, they were written for the Scribblers' amusement, to entertain my family and friends, and for myself. Soon, the urge to write took a stronghold, and I was compelled to create even more odd and wonderous stories.

The result is this collection of admittedly quirky, dark, and sometimes humorous tales that examine the human psyche. Why do we make the choices we make? How do we differentiate between right and wrong? What would we do if we were sure no one would ever find out? My stories explore those questions and many more, as filtered through the mind of a former Intelligence Officer now living in paradise.

PART I
SPYING

What does a jihadist bomber, two snipers, a disastrous dinner, and a gathering of senior intelligence officers in Bulgaria have in common? At first, the connection may not be clear, but together they provide insight into the complex world of international governments. It's an area that is often misunderstood by most civilians, but upon closer inspection, the themes are universal.

1. The Deep State

The veterinary clinic was in a rather nondescript building in McLean, Virginia, a small suburb just outside Washington, D.C. The black limo that pulled up in front was equally unremarkable in a city filled with government mucky-mucks whose status demands a bulletproof car with a driver.

Two men got out of the car, both wearing earpieces often seen in those guarding the president or other important people. One of the men opened the door of the limo. Out jumped a black spaniel-type dog. The man hooked a leash to the enthusiastic canine and walked into the clinic. The other followed carrying a small box.

On entering, they were immediately greeted by the vet. All the employees had been given the morning off. The doctor took the dog into the operating room and began the process of sedating and preparing it for surgery. The two men waited in the adjoining room to keep an eye on what was happening. The doctor made a small incision in the chest of the dog and then went to the box that had been provided. He removed a small silver disc about the size of a quarter, slid off the plastic cover and inserted it into the incision, sewed up the skin and proudly examined his work. There was no evidence of the surgery.

Two hours later, the dog and the two men returned to the car and slowly drove into D.C. They had been advised to drop Bo off at the White House after his "routine exam." It took a day or so to calibrate the embedded receiver, but pretty soon conversations could be recorded. As Bo roamed through the White House, sounds could be clearly heard even when the dog was in the family quarters or the Oval Office.

Intelligence on President Obama's plans, comments on the election, critical observations about the Republicans, and any number of other subjects were discussed, including criticism of Hillary Clinton. All this information went to "the deep state" and was used to undermine the administration. The conversations obtained through Bo's transmitter were transcribed, given to the media, and attributed to a source inside the White House. Right wing radio, Fox News outlets, The Weekly Standard and a variety of other conservative media were given as much negative information as the deep state operatives could gather from Bo's intercepts. Nothing positive was reported.

What was happening? Apparently, there was an effort to undermine the elected government. Who were these people? They could best be described as anarchists trying to weaken the government and thus people's confidence in it. They were not ideological and had no fondness for the administration elected in November 2016. In fact, they intended to repeat the process of implementing another "fifth column approach" within the incoming administration.

The secret service agents that turned Bo into an intelligence collection system met again after the election of President Trump. They had received more instructions from the deep state.

One of them asked the other, "Does Trump even have a dog?"

2. The Loophole

A large convoy composed of the Washington press corps and White House staff left the city heading for West Virginia. There was a buzz of excitement. The new president was holding her first cabinet meeting to set the tone for the next four (and potentially eight) years.

The newly sworn-in cabinet was the most diverse in history; three blacks, two Hispanics, two Muslims, five white males (two straight and three gay), and two Asian lesbians.

The setting for the meeting was admittedly unorthodox. It was held in a large cafeteria. Tables were pushed together with the president seated at one end and cabinet members placed in order of department seniority. Coffee was served in plastic cups with a spork. There were no traditional utensils in sight.

The president stood up and welcomed the group to their first meeting. She was dressed in a bright yellow pantsuit. The cabinet members were in typical Washington business attire. Some of the staff members had been on the president's team when she was secretary of state. They wore varying shades of yellow.

When she turned to speak to the press corps, the letters US PLWV were clearly stenciled on the back of her outfit to identify the United States Penitentiary Lewisburg West Virginia.

The Supreme Court of the United States has yet to rule on whether a convicted felon can remain in the office of the president.

3. A Gold Mine

About five years ago, I sold my business for a tidy sum and moved my family to Vero Beach, Florida. The decision was easy not only because leaving the frozen north was appealing but because Vero is such a beautiful place. My family and I had spent several winter vacations in Vero and had become very fond of the town and particularly the island.

We decided to buy the nicest place we could afford. After visiting a number of houses with our eccentric real estate agent, we finally chose an older home in Riomar, a rather high-end area just south of the island village. I went all-out, joining an expensive golf club, buying a Porsche and living the high life. It was grand.

Things went along well for a couple of years and then I began to worry. The property taxes climbed higher, utilities were three times what I spent in the north, and my country club fees seemed to come due with increasing frequency. My new lifestyle was quickly eating up my savings, and there was no money was coming in. I needed to reassess my situation and either significantly cut expenses or find a new source of funds. Social security would not see me through.

I had no immediate plan for how to solve my financial dilemma. But one day as I sat watching television, I saw an advertisement for investing in gold. It mentioned getting gold bars and coins sent to your home by cashing in your IRA. I was not interested in buying gold, but I wondered who was making those purchases. A variety of ideas flooded my mind. How could I find out who the buyers were and what could I do with that information?

My grandson had once talked about "the dark web" and even showed me how to access it. I discovered it's an area of the Internet with all kinds of unsavory users who want to conceal their illicit activities—porn, gun running, bomb making, and on and on. It has several layers, all requiring their own password. Obviously, this web is heavily monitored by law enforcement and intelligence organizations, so I needed to take heed. My cover was that I belonged to a writing group, and I was known for my bizarre stories involving illegal and clandestine activities. Thus, my access was in the interest of research.

I put a note on one of the sites asking for help in writing a story about breaking into a company's secure database. I then sat back and waited. I used a throwaway phone acquired with a phony address as the contact number. Amazingly, I received several calls in answer to my inquiry. I indicated that I was writing a story about someone who wants to hack into a company computer system. One person was particularly knowledgeable. I told him I •wanted the customer list and order amounts from a company that sold gold ingots and coins. I identified the target and offered to pay him $3,000 for the information. The money would be paid in cash sent discreetly to an address he specified.

When he began to ask for details about how I would use the information, I told him it was the basis of a book I was writing, and I could afford the money because I had already received a sizeable publishing advance. I was not sure he believed me, but what difference would it make as long as he fulfilled the task and sent me the information I wanted? I was not about to pay him until his job was completed successfully.

Three weeks later I was checking my rented mailbox at a nearby package store (acquired under an alias, of course). There was a thick envelope inside. I opened it and found a list of customers who had purchased gold to be delivered to their home with another list of the amount each had spent. Now, what to do with that information? First, I obtained a money order for $3,000 that I mailed to my mysterious helper, hoping I'd never hear from him again.

I looked carefully at the list, paying particular attention to the mailing addresses. A couple of them were in the general vicinity of Vero Beach, one was in John's Island, another in the city and a third in Fort Pierce. Two of the buyers had made multiple purchases adding up to several hundred thousand dollars. What, if anything, was I going to do with this intel?

I had a couple of ideas, all clearly illegal and risky, but also promisingly profitable at the end. I could take up the profession of a burglar, but that meant I would need some new skills that could not be acquired at the local junior college: breaking and entering, safe cracking, etc. Or I could try to sell the information on the dark web and let others take the risk. But collecting payment could be tricky. Maybe I really should just write a book because this was not a bad plot.

Over the next few days, I weighed my options, one of which was to simply cut back on expenses. But all that gold out there was alluring, and I could not resist the temptation to put another ad on the dark web. Selling lucrative targets to adventuresome person that operates on the dark side. Again, I gave the number of my temporary phone.

It did not take long to get some calls, but now I had to ensure that I was not talking to an FBI agent trying to entice me into committing an illegal act and then slapping the handcuffs on me. How do you distinguish between a person posing as a criminal and the real thing? Surprisingly, the caller had that covered.

The man I spoke with said that his idea was to burgle a house in the area as a test, giving me the address after the break-in so that I could check the crime report section of the newspaper to verify that the robbery had indeed occurred. A bit extreme but at least I was reasonably sure the FBI would not think up such a scheme. So, we put the plan in motion.

Over the next few days, I carefully scoured the newspaper to see if there were reports of a robbery. Then one morning as I was eating breakfast and looking out my kitchen window, I saw a couple of police cars drive past. I went outside as they pulled up next door. I cautiously walked over and asked the policeman what was going on. He would only say that the house had been broken into while the owners were asleep. Fortunately, no one was harmed.

I was not particularly friendly with this gentleman and in fact he had once reported us to the association because our garbage cans were on the curb too long. He also told the neighbors that he thought our inflatable Christmas polar bear was gauche. Still, I didn't want to be responsible for his being robbed. Maybe it was a coincidence.

I scurried home after my brief conversation with the police just in time to hear the phone ringing. It was my burglar friend who asked what I thought of his handiwork next door. How had he found my home number and my address? He obviously knew more about me than I had intended, and that made me uncomfortable. I was worried that this may not be the last time I hear from my new friend.

The phone rang again. He reminded me that I had promised to give him some worthy targets for his next hit. He was eager to get started. I instructed him to call back in a couple of days and we would settle on what to do next.

Should I try to get rid of him or just join up and become a partner in crime? Perhaps I could find a way to warn the police that he was going to rob a house, get him arrested and keep from being involved in any criminal activity. But how? My new friend knew too much about me. Or did he? What exactly did he know? I had told him I knew of some good targets, but I had not indicated how I chose them.

What if I went to the police and said I was writing a novel and had contacted a burglar to get some real information on burglaries and that fellow had subsequently robbed a neighbor to prove he was the real thing? Working with the police, we could set up a trap for my "friend," giving him a target that would be placed under surveillance. The more I thought about this scheme, the more unrealistic it seemed. Another option, I could arrange a meeting with my burglar and murder him. No, I couldn't go through with that. Exasperated, I decided to join in the nefarious activity.

You may be surprised to know that partnership has worked for several years. Quite profitably, I might add. He turned out to be an interesting fellow, and we have become close friends as well as "coworkers." We average about 15 homes a year. We divide the take 50-50. I target, he conducts the operation, and I market the take. I never try to sell more than 10k in bullion or coins at a time to avoid suspicion. I travel extensively to gold dealers, seldom going to the same one twice. Sometimes I will trade bullion for coins or the other way around. So far it has worked well.

Who is the burglar? It turns out he is my neighbor. The one whose house was originally burglarized. He said he had been observing me for some time and had regularly hacked into my computer when my wife and I were not home. I asked him how he knew I was thinking about committing a crime.

He said, "It takes one to know one."

4. The Dinner from Hell

The Baker Award Dinner was scheduled for June 9th. Invitations had been sent out several months ahead, the award recipient was former FBI Director Mueller. The dinner was to be held at the Omni Hotel in DC, black tie, speeches, dinner and a chance to see old colleagues. I was a bit reluctant to spend over $1,000 for air travel and hotel, but I felt some interest in seeing old friends, and I had been given the Baker Award several years earlier so there was an implicit obligation.

The Baker Award was named after James Baker, a scientist, head of Bell Labs, and long-time advisor to presidents on issues related to technical collection, signals, and imagery. He and his fellow members were the moving force behind the CIA's development of the U-2 and the imagery and signals satellite systems. I was fortunate to have briefed the President's Foreign Intelligence Advisory Board (PFIAB) on Cuba and Soviet military in 1962 and 1963.

Getting ready for the dinner, I sent my old tuxedo off to the cleaners, and cobbled together the tie, cummerbund, cuff links and studs. The outfit seemed presentable although Jan had to make a contraption with a rubber band and a button sewn on to make the collar of the shirt big enough. The ensemble was a little disreputable, but it would do.

I was off to the Melbourne airport early in the morning, however, my knee was acting up and I had been using a cane or crutch. I decided to use the crutch, thinking it would help when walking down long airport concourses. Was I ever right! Melbourne was easy although I was on a very small aircraft. Luckily, I did sit next to an attractive woman from Vero who had worked in DC with people I knew in Homeland Security.

Arriving in Charlotte I had to leave the aircraft by stairway—hard to do with a crutch, small rolling suitcase and garment bag. Then a mile to walk from terminal E to terminal C. The Reagan National terminal was fine, and I took a cab to the Omni. I arrived about 2 p.m. and took a nap, planning to get into costume right at 6:00.

Then the problems began. The shirt with Jan's button/rubber band was ok, but it left too big a gap and my Scottish plaid tie kept falling off to one side. Ok, I can deal with that; I will just stand up straight and occasionally fix my tie. Then I put on the pants. They were not even close to fastening. I had cleaned the wrong ones. I called down to the front desk asking if they had a tailor in house. "Yes, she will be in first thing Monday." It was Saturday night. I then asked them for a pair of scissors and a sewing kit. Up came a sewing kit but no scissors. What to do?

I nearly decided to bag the whole thing and just stay in my room. But I thought, Hell, I'll just wear my brown khaki pants and pretend that's the new style. Off I went, a rickety old fart dressed like Emmett the Clown. Halfway down the front hall, my bowtie fell off! I casually picked it up and confidently balanced it back in its precarious position. Moving into the large reception room with several hundred people around, I again nearly turned around and went back to my room. Everyone looked just grand. Why had I come? I must have stood out like a straw man.

After standing in the center of the crowded room for a while, believing maybe no one would look down and notice my brown pants, a couple of old friends came up. One of them ended up guiding me around all evening. Neither said a word about my appearance. I spent the rest of the time before dinner standing in one spot in the center of the crowd.

I had decided to wear two of my medals on my tux. No one else among the 500 people made that decision. At one point someone came up and took a close look at one of the medals, holding it in his hand. The medallion fell to the ground.

Then dinner chimes rang, and I silently thanked God that I could sit down. My table was in the middle of the banquet room with seven other people. I knew two of them; the others knew of me. One was from Mitre and mentioned that he attended Dr. Schlesinger's memorial service where I had shared my memories of Jim. An old friend, the former ambassador with North Korea, sat across from me. Nothing untoward happened except my bowtie again fell off. I gave up and put it in my pocket. They kept putting a bottle of white wine in front of me. Concern over my costume soon faded.

The evening continued, despite Mueller's absence, with one of his friends accepting the award for him. After a few remarks, the event ended. Thank God I had a room in the same hotel.

Up early, I took a plane back to Melbourne. Flying was ok coming back except maneuvering the steps to change planes at Charlotte was precarious to say the least. I swore it was my last flight through Charlotte and my last attendance of a Baker Award Dinner. To make certain, I threw away my tux.

5. The Plot

The world was in disarray. A number of countries had leaders that were just too disruptive to be allowed to continue pushing the world to the brink. It was inevitable that someone would put a faction together to lay out a plan to get rid of the tyrants.

This particular group met in a safe house just outside Washington, D.C. It began with the woman in charge saying, "We cannot have our fingerprints on this. Whatever we end up doing, it must not be traced back to us. This must appear to be a popular uprising."

What was the bill of particulars against the target? The list was long:

- He did not get into power through a legitimate democratic process.
- He was unfit to be in charge.
- He was crude and violent by nature.
- His policies were ruining the country.
- He did not have majority support in the country.
- Most critical, his actions were placing the world at risk of a major war.

The group carefully considered the unintended consequences. What were the chances they could end up with someone even less stable and harder to control than the "incumbent?" Would their actions trigger total, uncontrolled chaos? Were potential outcomes worse than doing nothing? Would it be better to wait it out, hoping for self-correction or internal changes?

The group decided that the best outcome would be a new leader that had some influence over policies that benefited the country, a change in leadership that appeared to have popular support and no foreign involvement.

They laid out specific actions aimed at achieving their goal. After agreeing on the details of a plan of action, the group broke up and the woman in charge reported back to the chairman of the Democratic Party. The plan to remove President Trump was put into motion.

6. Chinese Malware

Recent Article in Local Vero Beach Newspaper

The greatest transfer of wealth in the history of the world touches Vero Beach locals. As most of you know, Chinese, Russian, and Iranian hackers have been looting U.S. industrial secrets for several years. Breaking into computer systems of nearly every U.S. corporation, they have systematically recovered technical secrets on advanced electronics, chemical formulas, and an endless variety of sophisticated devices. This information allows China to avoid long and expensive development programs and profit from the work of others. This activity also has given them unique advantage in marketing and bidding.

Recent information provided by U.S. organizations involved in monitoring foreign hacking also has revealed the placement of disinformation and the destruction of information at the local level in the U.S. Several specific examples of malicious intervention in private information systems have been reported. One of the most egregious involved the Scribblers, a local writers' group in Vero Beach.

Gertrude, one of a dozen Scribblers, was personally attacked when her memoir was fundamentally changed. Rather than Jacksonville, her family was placed in northern Vermont. The revision describes her as an only child living with a mean and cranky uncle who did not like children. Gertrude has indicated that this interference in her life is most disturbing and has directly affected her well-being. She blames the president of China and has vowed not to buy any Chinese products in the future. She insists that she also will avoid Chinese restaurants and in a drastic act has decided that she will no longer help a young Chinese student who was on his way from Shanghai to live with her.

In another incident, a long-time Vero resident has discovered that large portions of a book he is writing on Ice Age man in Vero Beach have been significantly changed and portions even deleted from his computer. The new text indicates that the remains of five humans found at the Vero dig site have been positively associated with Ponce de Leon and consequently date to the 1500s, not the Ice Age. Mr. Johnson is formally complaining to the Chinese archaeological society, indicating that such shoddy scholarship is not acceptable in the U.S. He has also threatened to reveal the true story of Peking Man if apologies and compensation are not forthcoming. Mrs. Johnson's book was also tampered with and placed in the first person with some spicy additions to her narration.

The writings of other Sandfly Scribblers have been altered. A fascinating but unfinished story about an English dinner party by Kitty was crudely completed by an inarticulate hacker who only succeeded in wrecking the beautiful drama by having the dinner take place in Venice during the 1400s and the entire party being wiped out by the Black Plague. Suzan's wonderful tale about a famous playwright in the early 1900s was fundamentally compromised when a variety of statements were inserted indicating that the playwright was not gay. Elise's book on art instruction was altered when all her drawings were turned into stick figures, and her last chapter changed to admit that most people do not have a chance in hell of becoming artists. In an act of true deception, the hackers provided stories purportedly written by Charlotte and Nancy, when everyone knows they do not write stories.

The list of writers interfered with goes on. Eugene's intense recollections of his family in Ireland provided a dark picture of unloving relationships. It was stark in its portrayal of family members unable and unwilling to bend and in some cases acting purposely cruel. His stories were recast into the distorted picture of happy and encouraging parents, loving siblings, and a family that tried to help each other during difficult times. Another writer, Russ, was treated very poorly. Rather than a bureau chief for an important newspaper, he was cast as a scandal-chasing reporter for the National Enquirer. Articles about President Kennedy were replaced with erotic pieces about a movie star being impregnated by Martians and a story of sea monsters in Lake Michigan.

Fortunately, Pat's continuing story of his life was untouched because the hackers could not recover the documents from his computer. Dick Kerr's short stories were not altered, perhaps because they were already too strange.

The government has no explanation for the attack on the book club. Some Chinese experts, however, believe that the hackers found the individualism of the group alarming to the collectivist minds of the Chinese.

7. The Tube

Looking through the brass tube of the telescope, I could clearly make out the couple on the beach. The heavyset man was gesturing rather wildly, and the woman was staring into his face with tears running down her cheeks. They were middle-aged, wearing stylish walking clothes. The man's large mustache seemed out of proportion to his face, which was pinched and red. The woman was attractive but not beautiful. Her red hair was streaked with grey and drawn back into one of those schoolteacher buns.

I felt a bit the voyeur but was reluctant to put the glass down or move it from the couple. I remained trained on them. I read her lips and she said something like "You're the bastard." Then she slapped him without warning. The slap was delivered with considerable force and caused him to fall back backward. I had always wanted to slap him myself but never had the courage.

She began walking quickly up the path toward me and the man followed at a somewhat slower pace. I put the telescope in my pack as she climbed up the dune. It would be embarrassing if she found I had been watching their performance on the beach.

She walked up close, grabbed my shoulders and said, "Your father and I finally decided that you had to be told the truth."

8. Spy Stuff

In early November 2015, Gunter Schabowski died at the age of 80. He was the East German bureaucrat who inadvertently triggered the collapse of the Berlin Wall. As a spokesman for the ruling Politburo, he announced on television that travel restrictions on East German citizens had been lifted. He did not realize that there was an embargo on this announcement.

Within hours, the tide of people trying to cross the border was unstoppable and border guards gave up trying. Mr. Schabowski was expelled from the party shortly thereafter. After the reunification of Germany, he was sentenced to prison for his complicity in the shoot-to-kill policy enforced by border guards.

The report of Schabowski's death led to recollections about his boss—Lt. General Marcus Wolf—the head of German intelligence (Stasi) for many years.

I met General Wolf on two occasions—a gathering of a board for a new East European journal in Croatia in 2005 and a book signing in Sophia, Bulgaria, the next year. Wolf had served several years in jail after the unification of Germany, sentenced as traitor. That sentence was overturned because he was a citizen of East Germany, not the FRG. He retired as head of German intelligence in the late 1950s and became well-known as an author.

General Wolf and I had private conversations during our two meetings. He was particularly outspoken over what he considered the unfair treatment he received after the unification of Germany. He said he had acted in the interest of his country as a committed Communist. On several occasions—surrounded by former heads of French, American, Bulgarian, Croatian and Russian intelligence—he said there was no difference between his actions as head of the Stasi and the actions of other heads of intelligence. They all supported the policies of their countries.

At one point during one of his outbursts at a very public meeting celebrating the publication of a book on intelligence, I decided I had enough and said there was little comparability between his actions and those of Western intelligence services. We did not support or commit the kind of crimes against our citizens that Stasi regularly engaged in. Our efforts were directed at foreign countries, I said, not shooting people trying to escape, turning the state into a vast set of informers that crushed any sign of dissent and actively eliminating all the freedoms expected, even in the most authoritarian countries.

I would have had the same response to a similar comment from the heads of Russian or Bulgarian intelligence. All intelligence organizations respond to the requirements of their country. That was part of the point made by Wolf—he was just doing what he was required to do in support of his nation, just following orders and he should not be punished for doing that.

No intelligence organization has totally clean skirts when it comes to ethical or even moral issues. But the moral and ethical differences between the actions of Western intelligence services and those of the USSR and East Germany can be measured in miles, not inches.

9. Writer's Bloc

Sometimes it is difficult to come up with a story for the Monday morning writing group. But Dick had put down some notes in the computer and decided to develop them.

The plot centered on a rogue group in the White House that decided to run an operation to assassinate Kim Jong Un, the leader of North Korea. The story described a plan to recruit a member of the delegation accompanying Dennis Rodman to carry a bomb and place it near the president during a basketball exhibition in Pyongyang. The person recruited to place the bomb did not know that the timing mechanism gave him too little time to move away from the explosion.

Dick developed the story and printed out copies to take to the Monday gathering. He drove his golf cart down Sandfly Lane, toward a house down the street where a group called the Sandfly Scribblers met. A local gardener's truck pulling a trailer was stopped at Club Drive, and as he waited for it to move, a black SUV pulled onto Sandfly Lane and stopped opposite him. Two men jumped out and grabbed him, throwing him in the back seat of the SUV. Another man put down the ramp of the trailer and drove the golf cart onto it. Both vehicles then left the area going in different directions down Club Drive.

Two days later, the news went bonkers reporting what few details were known about an explosion in North Korea that killed the president and several senior Korean officials and injured some U.S. basketball players during an exhibition game. No group claimed responsibility, but there was speculation that only the Korean military would be able to place a bomb so close to the president.

In hindsight, it is clear that although Dick was keenly aware that the phones of U.S. citizens were being monitored, he did not realize that the strokes on his keyboard were being carefully recorded as well. Nor did he imagine that the story he had made up in his somewhat twisted mind would compromise an operation that was underway at that very moment.

10. An Autobiography in Bulgarian

During a meeting of senior retired intelligence officers in Dubrovnik in February 1999, the idea of a book containing the biographies of former chiefs and deputies of Western and former Bloc countries took shape. It was the brainchild of General Todor Boyadjiev, the former deputy of the Bulgarian intelligence service.

My first reaction was negative. I had retired from the CIA only six years earlier, and I was not sure that an autobiography was appropriate or even possible. But in the end, I was persuaded by my friend (who had a long association with Todor) my own ego, and the idea of leaving some historical documentation for my family. I completed the forty-page chapter and sent it to a CIA review board, and it was subsequently published in book form in 2000. I should add that it was initially published in Bulgarian; an English version came out six years later.

The book contained ten chapters. Seven written by former intelligence officers, and three other pieces: one written by George Tenet, the Director of Central Intelligence; one by Kim Philby, a deceased British turncoat; and an article by Miro Tudman from Croatia. The chapters were a mixed bag of commentary on intelligence and personal histories.

Most of the authors attended the book publishing event in Sofia in 2000. Sofia, the capital of Bulgaria, is an ancient city that predates the Roman Empire. As an honored guest, I was not given a suite in a relatively new hotel downtown and next to the area where the conference and book signing was held. I was put up in a historic house on a hill overlooking the city—a wooden structure built in the 1600s with ancient plumbing and a bed with rope strung under a thin mattress. The floors creaked in the slightest wind, shutters and doors banged, and the house seemed alive. Several times during the night I thought I heard people walking around inside although I knew I was the only occupant. The next morning, I walked down the hill to the city, passing a Roman colosseum where a group of actors were rehearsing.

The first event of the conference was a series of speakers talking about the "new" modern Bulgaria; one not under the yoke of Communism. A young man spoke about the evils of the previous regime and to my surprise, a group of middle-aged men in the audience—clearly former government apparatchiks—took off their shoes and begin pounding on the desks in front of them in protest. The young speaker did not miss a beat but continued to upbraid those unwilling to accept change. From that moment on when I attended speeches, I always thought about untying my laces, so I could quickly take off my shoes and pound on a table.

Most of the day involved speeches by those who had contributed to the book. Perhaps the most memorable talk was given by Marcus Wolf, the former head of East German intelligence, the Stasi. He clearly felt that the new, unified Germany was treating him unjustly. In his speech he said the causes of the East and the West were equally justified, that he had just carried out the wishes of his country and was as much a patriot as other speakers. I followed him on the podium and said I just could not accept his view that the actions of both sides during the Cold War were morally equivalent. I said the East German government and its policies and treatment of its people were evil. People who implemented those policies could not escape the association and blame. I am afraid I put a wet blanket over the ceremony, and I did get the cold shoulder from Wolf and some of the Bulgarians for the rest of the conference. But life is short and then you die, and in-between, you need to do what you think is right.

There was always a bit of uncertainty about who funded the conference and the book. I was introduced to Stephan, a "friend" of Todor, who I decided must be the patron. Stephan had all the characteristics of the East European mafia. He was driven around in a black Suburban with an armed driver and second man in the front and followed by a similar chase car. He was also accompanied by a beautiful and delightful "secretary" that looked like a former Miss East Europe. Stephan indicated that he was building a large resort on the Black Sea and invited my wife and I for a two-week visit. He would pay all expenses. He also offered to have his secretary and car take me on a tour of an ancient Orthodox monastery located an hour out of Sofia. I decided that the trip to the Monastery would be interesting, but the trip to the Black Sea resort might be a bit over the top. I could see the headline in *The Washington Post*, "Former Head of CIA's Trip to Resort on Black Sea Paid for by Bulgarian Mafia."

The trip to the monastery was very worthwhile. It was huge, with large living quarters for dozens of monks. It had been constructed in the 1200s. We spent several hours touring the buildings and grounds, which were heavily forested and crisscrossed by streams filled with live fish. After a delightful lunch and some excellent wine, the secretary and I made our way back to Sofia.

Maybe I should reconsider a trip to that Black Sea resort.

11. The Assignment

Nothing is more frustrating than waiting for the next assignment. You cannot hurry up the process, because "the powers that be" determine what you will do next. You are just an innocent babe waiting for instructions.

It is particularly frustrating to me because the last several assignments have been so intense. The most recent was as part of a force attempting to rescue the embassy staff under attack in Libya. I left Europe in a C-130, flew directly to Tripoli, and then got aboard a stealthy helicopter with a small special forces team for the flight to Benghazi. Although we were too late to save the ambassador and two SEALs at the CIA annex, we managed to rescue the rest of the team. The firefight was heavy, and the return to the airport and then Tripoli a bit hairy.

Of course, I have been involved in many similar incidents over the years: trying to push back the Taliban in Afghanistan while on horseback, tracking down and helping to kill Osama, rescuing a captain captured by pirates, tracking Saddam to his hideaway in Iraq and perhaps most important, ending the Cold War. I must break off now because they are coming with news. Damn, this is exciting.

"Today, you are going to serve the mashed potatoes in the food line for the homeless."

12. The Snipers

They were only 1,000 yards apart, but miles different. U.S. Army Staff Sgt. Michael Rose grew up in Ohio, had been in the army for 15 years and was a sniper serving his second tour in Afghanistan. Lying in a shallow depression, he was covered by a camouflage sheet that was blanketed with branches and dirt. The harness of a Barrett sniper rifle loaded with a single .50 caliber cartridge was strapped around his shoulders.

Lying perfectly still, Michael had been in position for three hours, staring at the entrance to a small cave directly across the valley. He had seen no movement, but thought he had a glimpse of light reflected off what could have been binoculars or a telescopic sight. He had adjusted his sights to accommodate a slight wind and lay in wait until a target presented itself.

Volunteer Gulbidin Sjadar was lying at the edge of the shadows just inside the mouth of the cave across the valley. He had grown up in Libya and been recruited to fight in Afghanistan just over two years ago. When he arrived in Afghanistan, he was trained as a sniper and equipped with an old but very serviceable .300 Winchester rifle with a sniper scope.

Gulbidin had been in position for an hour or so, and he was carefully searching the mountain directly across from his position. He knew there were some American troops in the area because he had seen movement some hours before he positioned himself. He adjusted the sights on his rifle to fire at any target of opportunity.

Both men saw the other move slightly at about the same time. That allowed them to focus in on a particular spot. The circular patterns of the rifle muzzles and telescopic sights were not immediately apparent, but both men thought they could see shapes that seemed to stand out from the surrounding rocks and dirt.

Each looked down their telescopic sights, held their breath and slowly pulled the triggers of their rifles. The two shots occurred simultaneously, so close together that it sounded like a single rifle firing.

Three days later, Mr. and Mrs. Rose were informed that their son had been killed during an operation in Afghanistan. God bless him.

Sjadar's parents did not receive word of their son's death for more than a month.

Allahu akbar.

13. The Bomber

The explosion was heard blocks away, and shortly thereafter a column of smoke could be seen over the Israeli bus station. Everyone knew immediately that there had been another suicide bombing.

A man had boarded a fully loaded bus and detonated the bomb, killing himself and a dozen others and injuring many more. The carnage defied description. The bomb had been loaded with shrapnel—bolts, pieces of metal and ball bearings—and even pieces of the bomber's body served as projectiles of death. The bus had been a death trap.

I was the bomber, and I do not regret the deaths and injuries I inflicted. For more than 70 years, the Israelis have treated Palestinians as less than human. They have humiliated them again and again. Those on the bus deserved to die, and this incident offers another lesson to the Israelis that things must change.

I was 22 years old, born in Gaza to working-class parents. I attended school for 10 years but never was able to get a full-time job. My oldest brother was killed in the first intifada in 1987, and my youngest brother is in an Israeli jail after being rounded up in an operation trying to stop Palestinians from tearing down the wall built along the Israeli border.

I did not pay much attention to politics, but I remember when the Israelis withdrew their forces from Gaza in 2005. At age 14, I joined a small group studying the Koran at the local mosque where I was recruited as courier. I watched as the Israelis bombed the headquarters of Hamas in 2008 and saw their tanks fire into houses, killing innocent women and children. We could not become Israeli citizens and could not have an independent state—we were in limbo, a non-people.

I knew something had to be done and realized that I would have little or no power to make a difference. A jihadist group took me under its wing and told me how I could change from being a powerless individual to someone who would be remembered by friends and mentioned as a hero in morning prayers. They told me about other martyrs who had given their lives and convinced me that my death was worth more than my life.

The actual training took about a week. During that time, I was placed in an apartment along with my instructors and a Koran. A video was made of me wearing the explosive vest, and I was told that $150 would be paid to my parents.

I was driven out of Gaza to the Israeli bus depot. As I boarded the bus, I looked at the men, women and children already seated. They glared at me with something bordering on hatred, or at least disdain—a poor Palestinian wearing his stupid keffiyeh. They did not deserve my pity, only my hatred. Empathy was something a Palestinian could not indulge in until there was fundamental change.

I did not have second thoughts as I pushed the plunger on the vest.

PART II
SURPRISE

Sometimes it is someone sneaking upon on you and yelling "Boo." Often it is the inability to see around corners, to anticipate or to imagine things outside your experience. An intelligence officer is often faced with this kind of uncertainty because the world is seldom neatly predictable. While history sometimes repeats itself, it often plows new ground. Stories with a surprise ending can be shocking, disturbing or just interesting.

14. The Car Awaits

I had lost my job at a major manufacturer of plastics products. The company I worked for had been "acquired" by another company, and I was redundant. It was a bit of a shock because I held a rather senior position and was feeling very secure with a nice salary and, I thought, good prospects. They gave me a generous severance pay, which meant I could look for another position without feeling too much pressure. But I did have a large mortgage, a high-end wife and two children nearing college age.

I decided to fly to New York and visit some old friends who might give me a lead on a new position. So, I was off to the city with no objective in mind but confident something would turn up.

Arriving in New York, I made my way to the baggage area and waited for my suitcase. Looking around, I saw a sign held by a driver with my name—John O'Brien—printed on it. An interesting coincidence, but I knew of no reason why a car was sent to pick me up.

I had on a few occasions seen airport limo drivers holding signs that had my name printed on a card. After all, the name John O'Brien is not unusual. It had occurred to me that it would be interesting to go up and announce myself and see where the car took me. But until this moment I had always been reluctant to take such a silly action. Why not? I thought. Who knows what could happen?

I walked up to the driver and confidently said my name. I held my breath for just a second, worried that he might know the person he was picking up. But he quickly took my luggage and walked me out to where he had parked the limo, opened the door to the back seat, beckoned me in, and then deposited my bag in the trunk of the car. For better or worse, I was committed.

Sitting back comfortably in the leather seat and after making some inane comment of the weather, I had a panic attack. What if the intended passenger called the driver asking why he was not outside the baggage area? A second later the driver's phone rang, and he answered on speakerphone. Was it his real passenger? No, I heard a woman ask if he had picked up his passenger. Safe for another moment.

Of course, I did not know where we were headed and did not want to ask. More than half an hour later, we pulled up outside the front door of a large modern building with a sign that read Philo Plastics. I had heard of them. It was considered a very aggressive competitor of the company that had purchased mine. What a coincidence. At least I was knowledgeable about the industry; perhaps there might be a job opening fitting my background.

Waiting outside the front door was a trim young woman who called out my name and asked me to follow her into a waiting elevator. Off to the top floor—26. I was getting in deeper and deeper, but at this point did not know how to extract myself. Up to this point, I could claim that it was a case of mistaken identity rather than some scam.

Getting out of the elevator, we walked up to a woman who was the executive assistant of the boss. She introduced herself and welcomed me by saying how eager Mr. Stein, the owner of the company, was to meet me and how he had enthusiastically read my resume.

I was taken in and introduced to Mr. Stein, a man about my age. He got up from his desk, extended his hand and gave me a warm smile. Then quickly he motioned that I should sit down. He did not offer any pleasantries about my flight, for which I was grateful. I did not know where he thought I came from.

I desperately needed to know something about Mr. Stein and his business if this interview was going to be anything but a farce. So, I began asking him questions about how he had started the company and where he wanted it to go. I opened a floodgate of information. He was the sole owner, president and CEO; had no board of directors, and a dear friend who recently died had been his deputy. We talked about management philosophy, some of the business problems he saw on the horizon, the financial condition of the company, orders, backlog, cash flow, profit, employee compensation, retirement concerns, and a host of other business issues.

After a couple of hours of conversation, he leaned over, looked me in the eyes and said, "I have had several interviews, but most of them wanted to talk about themselves, not the company. I like your approach and think you might be a good fit as my deputy." Then he leaned back in his chair and said, "What do you think?"

I began by saying, "Mr. Stein, do you believe in serendipity?" He nodded. "Everything you mentioned about your company—its products, its outlook, its problems—I am acquainted with those. I also have the engineering and manufacturing background in plastics that tends to fit your needs. I'm also better at being a deputy than a boss. There is only one problem that you might consider major."

I then explained how when I saw the limo driver with a sign with a name the same as my own, I somehow allowed myself to see what would happen. I explained that I needed a job and convinced myself that coming to Philo Plastics was my destiny.

"Call me Bob," Mr. Simon said. He then got up, came from behind his desk, and motioned me over to a more comfortable chair.

"You are the John O'Brien that my limo driver was told to pick up. I know a great deal about you and the company that my chief competitor recently acquired. I was surprised that you were let go. I generally have people who work for me in all the other plastics companies, and they informed me that you were exceptional. I thought the interview went well even though you did not realize I knew who you were. I also found that you proved to be a good sounding board for my thinking through the problems and opportunities facing us at Philo Plastics. You actually listen, and you're honest. Well, honest to a point. You're also adventurous. Those are good qualities."

He then got up and went to a credenza, opened it and asked, "You want a drink? I like scotch. How about you?" I mumbled that scotch on the rocks would be fine. After he toasted my drink with his and sat down, he said, "The salary I am willing to offer you would be a 30 percent increase over what you made at your old company. Plus, there are opportunities for bonuses and stock options depending on performance. What do you say? I need you to come to work in seven days, no later, because I am off to China for a few weeks on business."

I looked at my drink. "Could you make that a double please, Mr. Simon?"

He smiled. "Call me Bob."

15. The Ticket

It was beautiful. The resort was located on a small island covered with palm trees and rich green foliage. The buildings were bungalow style with grass roofs and wide eaves. There were no cars on the island; movement was by foot or small electric golf carts, consequently it was wonderfully quiet.

Every evening most of the 200-odd guests gathered around the pool or in the dining room for drinks followed by a tropical dinner broiled fish or shrimp and fresh fruit. The gathering was subdued, with most of the people talking about how they spent their day and what they intended to do next. There were no raucous voices or loud laughter.

I found it particularly interesting that when talking to the various groups around the pool, there were never references to past experiences; no bragging about visiting some great site or strutting about some personal accomplishment. It was as if the interests of each individual were totally focused on what was happening at that moment, what their fellow visitors were experiencing. They seemed to have little interest in the past. Most of the guests were Asian, predominately Chinese. There were very few Westerners.

It was particularly educational to be one of the few non-Asians at the resort. The Chinese included several artists and their families. What made it even more interesting was that all the artists were involved in calligraphy. I knew nothing about calligraphy and decided to learn a bit by spending some time with this rather unusual group. I learned that calligraphy involved writing letters or numbers, often with a single stroke, and that it grew out of the art of copying Chinese characters.

At one point in our discussion, an artist asked me for a piece of paper on which to illustrate the point he was making. I fumbled through my pockets and found the stub of an airline receipt. As I was handing the receipt to the artist, I looked at it carefully: Malaysian Airline Flight 370, Kuala Lumpur to Beijing.

That flight disappeared in 2017 and has never been found.

16. The Seduction - part 1

I was sitting in the bar of the hotel drinking my usual, a dirty martini. I enjoyed looking around the bar at the assembled patrons: couples gazing into each other's eyes, others reluctant to look at each other directly, and singles hoping to catch someone's eye, anyone's.

I often traveled alone and usually preferred to dine by myself, muse about life, and be the "observer," a bit like one of the characters in a Camus novel. Then I saw her across the room. Smart-looking, a smile as she talked to the waiter, probably in her mid-to-late thirties although I was never good at guessing the age of women. She ordered a martini, but from a distance I could not tell if it was dirty. I laughed to myself as I had a naughty thought. I watched her but tried not to stare. Soon our eyes met, and I raised my glass and gave her my best smile.

I sat there wondering what to do next and began to doodle on my napkin. Looking down, I realized I was writing all the synonyms for "affair"—tryst, assignation, coupling, hooking up. I had fantasized about some wild fling in the past but was always very careful about putting myself in the situation where I would have to fish or cut bait.

I had no end game in mind when I approached her table and said, "I would like some company for dinner tonight. Would you join me in the hotel restaurant?" Pretty cool and very grown up. At least I thought I did not appear as though I had just fallen off the turnip wagon. To my surprise she nodded her head and with a wide smile said, "That would be much better than dining alone." I introduced myself and she did likewise. Becky. Her last name never reached my ears, I was too busy looking at her face and even more directly at her rather low neckline. We went into the dining room seemingly as comfortable as couples who have known each other for some time.

Dinner was delightful. She was an executive secretary in town with her boss and had a free evening. I told her I was a foreign policy consultant attending a conference—close enough to the truth so I would not get tangled in lies. We hit it off well, and I was beginning to think about how to continue the evening.

We had dessert and an after-dinner drink. With considerable trepidation, I asked if she would like to finish our conversation over a bottle of champagne in my suite. Much to my surprise she agreed, although a bit too quickly, I thought. What had I gotten myself into? Like the dog that catches the car, what do I now? Well, in for a pence, in for a pound.

We finished our drinks. I paid the bill and we took an elevator to my suite on the 15th floor. Fortunately, it did not take long for room service to arrive, bearing an ice bucket with a bottle of champagne. I thought about the TV ad that showed someone opening a bottle of bubbly with a sword but chose the more conventional method.

We drank a toast to us. What should I do next? A kiss, an embrace? Or should I just say, "Let's take off all our clothes and hop in bed?" No! I had this compulsion to talk about the crisis in the Middle East. For a while she nodded her head and then occasionally made a comment. My soliloquy went on for some time; I realized a *long* time. I really don't know how long I talked. I excitedly told her about the fighting in Syria and the successes of ISIS and asked her if she knew that the current leader's father has totally destroyed a city to put down a revolt in the 1970s. I could not remember the name of the city and while Googling my iPhone to get the answer, I heard her say, "You have got to be kidding." When I looked up, she was slipping not into something more comfortable but out of the room, carefully closing the door.

When I read this story to the Scribblers, a couple of them decided to write their own version. Their stories follow.

17. The Seduction - part 2

by Gertrude Terry

As I entered the lobby, I realized I was not familiar with this hotel and its layout, but that didn't really bother me. I had traveled all over the world and one commercial five-star hotel was the same as the next. The marble floors, the crystal chandeliers, the bank of elaborate elevators, the gold banister of the curved marble stairway leading to the mezzanine. Ninety percent of its patrons were on an expense account, so damn the cost.

I headed for the ladies' room to freshen up. The brutal wind from the Uber to the doorman's greeting had played havoc with my hair, and the buttons on my jacket needed loosening in order to fluff the silk ruffles that allowed a deeper cleavage before heading to the bar where I hoped they could make a decent Cosmo (Grey Goose and Cointreau, and wouldn't it be lovely if they had fresh lime). I could definitely use one, maybe two, after the week I'd had.

Five airports in five cities in seven days. I was getting too jaded for this. I needed to start thinking about extricating myself from the stress of my assignments but hadn't come up with an acceptable, viable reason without leading to what could possibly become difficult complications. Besides, I still found my work exciting, stimulating. I had to confess, even if only to myself, that I craved the adrenaline rush of deadlines and precise timing. The violent action movies of my childhood I had seen with my father (I was the son he never had), had been exhilarating, and I knew at an early age that I wanted to be in the thick of the action, any action.

As the alert waiter guided me to a small table, we spoke briefly, he nodded and was off to fill my specific drink order. It didn't take long for me to hone in on the man at the bar with the roving eye. So easy to spot. If he'd had an "X" on his forehead, he couldn't have been more obvious. He was just who I was looking for. It wasn't long before we made brief eye contact. He smiled. I turned my head slightly, but not before lowering my eyes and giving my well-practiced shy smile in return. It never failed.

It wasn't long, of course, before he came over and asked me to join him for dinner. I could not have been more reluctantly charming with my acceptance. We went through the usual exchange of who we were and what we did. His foreign policy consulting business and my mission to procure international sites for my demanding bosses seemed to fit nicely.

After what seemed an interminably long and boring dinner of mostly desultory conversation, I was not surprised, as it fit my plans perfectly, to be asked to join him in his suite on the 15th floor for a bottle of champagne. I paused just long enough for him to fidget. Then with a genuine desire to get it over with, I accepted. At least there'll be some champagne! A great way to end an evening.

Sipping from my fluted glass, I listened to an endless treatise on the Middle East, some of which I thought, in another situation, might be construed as a little loose talk. He never seemed to realize that I knew more about what he was droning on about than he did. Finally, he went to Google something on his iPhone that he felt was vital to his dissertation. Was he really that stupid? Some jerks never catch on. I said, "You've got to be kidding," and got up to leave. The last thing he saw as I was carefully closing the door was the point of the silencer on my gun as I shot him on that imaginary "X", right between his eyes.

The door clicked shut.

18. The Seduction - part 3

by Kitty Kennedy

It had been a long flight and I was relieved to settle into my table in the hotel bar. I had stayed here many times, and it felt like a corner of home.

"Hello, Mrs. Connell, nice to see you again. What can I get for you?" the waiter said.

"Hello, Jack, I'd love a martini."

"What style?

"Surprise me; I'd love to be surprised. No more decisions for me today, thank you."

As I leaned into the comfortable high-backed chair, I saw a man sitting at the far end of the bar. Nice looking, well dressed, and he seemed comfortable in this setting. Probably the type who was comfortable in any setting. Jack brought my drink and as I raised my glass to take the wonderful first sip, my eyes drifted over to the man at the bar again, and he smiled and raised his glass toward me.

I sat back, took a deep breath, and reviewed some of the day. It had been a long one. Yes, in the end I was happy to have been included in this series of meetings. I'm VP of Marketing after all, but it looked like marketing was about to get a big boost. In fact, the reason for this final stop on this trip was to be introduced to the CEO.

Halfway through the martini, the man from the bar approached my chair. "Hello. I hope you don't think this is rude, but I am having dinner alone and I would like some company. I wondered if you would like to join in me in the hotel restaurant?"

I looked at him for a moment, decided that he would be good company, and said, "Yes, that would be much better than dining alone." On the way to dinner it was established that I was Becky and he was Bill.

Dinner was delicious, and he was a good companion. During dinner, I smiled as he told me that he was a foreign policy consultant attending a conference. I told him I was an executive secretary. Close enough to the truth. No one meeting a stranger in a bar tells the whole truth.

When dinner was over, he insisted on paying the bill, saying his expense account was enormous. Unusual for me in this situation, I said, "Yes." I thanked him for dinner, the good company and good conversation, and we walked into the lobby.

He said it was early and asked if I would like to come to his suite for champagne and more conversation. I stared at him. In these situations, before—and they did happen to me as I traveled so much—I would have said no. But this time I felt comfortable enough to say yes. He smiled but looked surprised. It turned out we were staying on the same floor.

After room service delivered and we were sitting comfortably on the sofa, we drank a toast to each other. After an awkward moment, the conversation started up again. He seemed to have considerable interest in the Middle East and talked at length about the crisis there. I nodded and asked the occasional question. It was a comfortable dialogue, and I felt like I did learn something.

When he began talking about the revolt in Syria in the 1970s, I started to feel it was time to say good night, go back to my room and check e-mail. At that moment, he started to Google some details about the Middle East on his iPhone. It looked like the evening was about to be extended, so I put my glass on the table. That was when I noticed that a business card had dropped out of his pocket and landed face-up on the sofa. I glanced down and said aloud, "You have got to be kidding." I could not help myself.

I stood up and without a word, walked toward the door of the suite, opened it and gently closed the door behind me. My heart was beating fast with the resulting adrenaline surge that always accompanies shock. The name on the card was William P. Maitland, and a corporate logo adorned the top of the card.

I had just had my first meeting with the new CEO of my company.

19. The Insurance Policy

We were beginning to run low on savings. Mortgage payments, medical bills, and just the normal cost of day-to-day living amounted to more than the income we received from social security, interest on savings and a modest retirement. My wife still insisted on going to France every year for a painting class. Something had to be done, and quickly.

Then I saw the advertisement on television. "Sell your life insurance and use the money to pay bills and live well!" It made a lot of sense; we did not need money after we passed on, we needed it now! My wife was adamantly against selling our insurance, and it was in both our names. She wanted to protect it for the children.

Nevertheless, when she went on her painting holiday, I decided to follow up on the idea of selling our insurance policy. Looking at the phone book I saw an ad by a local company that bought insurance policies, paying money up front. It seemed like a sensible thing to do despite my wife's reservations.

I decided to visit the company and see what I could do with our $100,000 policy. My expectations were moderate realizing that they would essentially be paying me for the policy but would need to wait until I died before they could collect the proceeds. And I planned to live for a considerable period of time...on their dime.

The insurance company was located on the second floor of a two-story brick building. Not an impressive establishment, a bit run down and in need of painting. I walked cautiously up the stairs to the office and was surprised at the comfortable surroundings; leather chairs, paintings on the walls, and rather expensive oriental rugs on polished hard wood floors. The company seemed to be prospering.

I was sent in to see an "advisor" who began asking a variety of questions: how old I was, my general health, the type of policy I had, the amount of insurance, and a few others. After referring to a couple of documents and typing on his computer, my "advisor" said I probably would receive about $60,000 from my policy, or two thirds of its face value. I told him I would send the paperwork since I had at least initially decided it was a reasonable deal.

I waited a few days and then called the company to find out the status of the deal. My "advisor" came on the line and in a very irritated voice said, "You have been wasting our time; your wife cashed in the policy several weeks ago using another company."

Suddenly, things clicked in my mind. My wife had not wanted me to take her to the airport, instead she drove her car. She also seemed vague about the time of her flight. I checked her closet and found that most of her clothes were missing. A quick call to the bank indicated that all our savings had been withdrawn.

I wonder if she is coming back?

20. For a Good Time Call

Driving from the airport to Vero Beach, I needed to telephone friends and tell them I was running late. My cell phone was out of power, but as I passed a service station, I noticed a rare pay phone on an outside wall and took a quick turn.

I made my call and said I would be an hour or so late. As I hung up the phone, I saw a small note written in marker on the wall beside the phone. It said "For a good time call 772-231-5677. An intellectual discussion, not phone sex." There was a drawing of a brain next to the note. On a whim, I wrote down the telephone number on a scrap of paper and shoved it in my pocket.

Several days went by, and I forgot about the incident. Looking over junk I had taken out of my pockets, I saw the note. Curious about who wrote on the payphone wall and what they really wanted, I decided to call.

The voice over the phone was hoarse and gravelly, but not clearly masculine or feminine. "Hello, what can I do for you?" I hardly knew what to ask, so, I began by saying, "I saw your note next to a telephone and decided to find out what you meant by an intellectual discussion." There was a pause, and the response was, "It meant exactly what it said.

I have no companions and few acquaintances, but I enjoy talking and am particularly fond of philosophy and politics, so I hoped someone with similar interests would call. I have placed ads in newspapers, but the only people who responded were either cranks or mentally unstable. I asked someone to put some graffiti notices up at telephones around the area."

Thus, we began a series of telephone conversations that went on for weeks and then months. We talked about many intriguing subjects: history, literature, philosophy, and current events. We never talked about personal matters and although I wasn't positive that my interlocutor was male, I decided to refer to my conversationalist as "him."

It was clear from the beginning of our relationship that he was my intellectual superior. On nearly any subject he would quickly get to the nub of the issue and express his conclusions clearly and succinctly. He was brilliant. I looked forward to our conversations with intensity and enthusiasm.

After a couple of months, I became increasingly curious about my new "friend." Who was he? What was his background? Where did he live? I decided to do a little detective work. Using his telephone number in a reverse directory, I found his address and was astonished to discover that it was the State Psychiatric Institute for the Criminally Insane.

21. The Accident

I was always a careful observer, sometimes even a bit obsessive about it. I was particularly interested in what others said about me. Every offhand remark or criticism and any slight or comment about my behavior was meticulously noted.

I watched my parents particularly close for signs of favoritism toward my brother and sister. And I secretly listened to them talking about me by hiding on the steps when they thought I was in bed, or at the edge of the patio as they had their evening drinks.

During one of these spying sessions, they were laughing and said that I was an accident, the result of a second martini. At first, I did not understand, but they went on to say that they really did not want to have another child, and, in fact, I had turned out to be a big disappointment. They were very cruel, describing me as a bit slow both mentally and physically, and often unable to make decisions.

After that, I paid far more attention to what they said, both to me and about me. I realized that I was not their favorite, in fact, they were not even fond of me, let alone loved me. I was dreadfully unhappy.

One night I was up late reading by the light of a small kerosene lamp. I had just finished a story and gotten up to put the book back on the shelf in the library. I tripped as I went by the staircase leading upstairs where my family was asleep. The lamp fell, spreading burning kerosene at the foot of the stairs. I stared at the flames and broken glass. I wanted to call for firemen but could not find the telephone. I wanted to put out the flames but could not seem to move quickly enough, and I was uncertain about what I should do. I wanted to cry out and warn everyone, but my voice cracked. Before I could do anything, the fire had spread up the stairs and the entire upper floor was in flames. My entire family died in the fire.

It was an accident.

22. The Beard and the Deal with the Devil

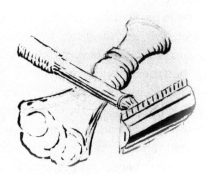

I started growing my beard because I was getting bored with my life. I did not know how attached I would become to that thatch of white facial hair, or how it would change my attitude and my life.

After my whiskers reached a reasonable length, I began to glance at myself in mirrors and windows as I walked by. Somehow, I seemed larger and more interesting. I had greater self-confidence and over time took on a kind of Walter Mitty personality, imagining myself in various adventures: helping maidens in distress, stopping bank robbers, sailing a four-mast ship in rough seas, and having madcap affairs with wild, tiger-like women. I was cool with it.

Life seemed more vital. People stopped me on the street merely to engage in conversation. Animals seemed attracted to me, particularly little dogs that would bark at my heels. I started to get more telephone calls asking for contributions to drives for curing various medical ailments and my opinion on political issues. I received an increasing number of pop-up ads on the internet. People looked at me with different eyes, and I could tell that they were impressed because they usually made quiet asides to their companions. I was cool with it.

Other aspects of my life changed. The writers' group on Sandfly thought my new stories were remarkably clear and bordered on brilliant. The local magazine *32963* asked me to do articles on foreign policy, replacing Charles Krauthammer. My speaking agenda expanded, and people were eager to pay the price for talks at Riverside and the Emerson Center. Success was in the air. I was cool with it.

At the morning market, I carefully watched men with white beards and then mentally compared their beards to mine. I thought most of the beards made them look older, and they were generally a bit scraggly and unkempt. Not at all like my beard, which was quite handsome and kept trim by a local barber.

My wife hated the beard and often said I looked like the Unabomber. She refused to kiss me except on the head and continually made rude remarks about facial hair. She just could not accept my beard and even disliked my new, more confident personality. I put up with considerable abuse, a lot of carping, and even some threats. Finally, she wore me down, and reluctantly I went to a barber to have the beard removed. I could not bear looking into the mirror at the barbershop even when the barber looked a little alarmed as he removed the last whiskers. I was not cool with it.

I walked into my house and when my wife looked at me, she turned pale, and a frightened look came over her face. I quickly ran into the bathroom and peered into the mirror. You cannot imagine the horror that overcame me. I looked like death warmed over, with a red rash and heavily wrinkled skin. My nose was hooked and my teeth uneven and discolored. My chin was very weak, and my cheeks sunken in like I had eaten a lemon. I had aged under that beautiful beard the same way Dorian Gray's portrait had aged in the attic while the subject stayed young.

Obviously, the agreement I had made with the devil was null and void.

23. Please Reverse the Charges

I was terribly lonely. The few friends I had were dead, had gone to live with their children in some remote town in Ohio, or were institutionalized. My wife passed away several years ago, and my children were all too busy to visit. They had their own lives to live. I was too old to start a new career and working for some charity spooning out the evening meals seemed worse than being alone. I felt useless and pitiful.

As I sat in my usual chair feeling sorry for myself, I happened upon an ad in the newspaper. "Need to talk to somebody? For a small fee you can speak with a counselor who will bring you fresh ideas and new hope. You will find our experienced and understanding personnel remarkably frank and friendly."

My first reaction was to remember a book that I had read sometime in the 1960's—what was it—*Miss Lonelyhearts* by Nathanael West. It was one of the most depressing books I had ever read, and one of the best. I was a bit irritated that I even considered the idea of talking to a total stranger who knew nothing about me and paying for the privilege. I remembered "Miss Lonelyheart" laughing over the pathetic letters he received.

But the idea preyed on my mind for several days. What did I have to lose but a few dollars, and maybe the process would keep me going? Who knows, I might even learn something.

I found the paper in the garbage and located the ad. It was a local number. I dialed and was asked who I wished to talk to. After saying this was the first time that I had called, the operator said it would cost me $25 for fifteen minutes and $50 to register. He then would put me through to Ellen—my counselor. Kind of expensive for a tightwad like me, but I gave him my credit card information and then was connected with my counselor, Ellen.

This is from Ellen's point of view:

"Ellen, there is another sucker on line 3 waiting to talk with you. See if you can keep a hold of this one so we can collect a bit of information and perhaps make a score. You didn't have enough patience with the last customer," said Sam.

"Ok, ok, Sam. I got it. Hello? This is Ellen. I am looking forward to talking with you. What is your name?" Pause.

"Hi, Bob, why do you to think you need to talk with a counselor?" Checks her social media accounts on her iPhone.

"Do you have any close friends?" Looks at the clock.

"I understand how difficult it can be as you get older, losing a wife, friends begin to die off. New friends are hard to make when you don't work. Do you have any hobbies or belong to clubs or a church?" Takes a sip of diet cola.

"Coin collecting, particularly collecting gold coins, sounds like a great hobby, although it seems like a hobby where you would not meet many people. What started your interest in coins?" Sees manager making motions to extend the conversation.

"Your career as a broker in rare metals must have been quite challenging and involved travel throughout the world. Your family probably was very interested in your travel overseas and in your job as a broker for gold, silver, and other rare metals." Shrug.

"I am sorry to hear that. Sometimes our jobs are not of interest to family or friends who focus on their own interests." Oops.

"We have nearly used up our 15 minutes. Why don't you call back at the same time the day after tomorrow? Good! Bob, I have enjoyed talking with you and look forward to our next visit." Hangs up the phone.

Sam said, "Ellen, I think you've got him."

I thought about my conversation with Ellen. She was so pleasant and understanding. I knew she was hired to talk with lonely people, but I believed that she really did understand me and my problems. Sure, she was getting paid to be nice to the customer, but it seemed like there was more to it than that. Besides, even if was all an act, I felt a lot better after the call than before. I certainly intended to call her again.

And I did call again and again, and soon I was talking to Ellen three or four times a week. We became quite comfortable discussing personal things. She told me about her childhood and growing up, and naturally I opened up, telling her things that I never even told my immediate family. She was very interested in my experience as a buyer of rare metals. My wife had always thought my business was terribly boring.

I sat thinking about Ellen after one of our conversations, wondering where she lived and what she looked like. I did not want to ask her outright, although I got the impression she lived somewhere along the beach. I remembered reading about how people could find out the address of the person if they had the telephone number. Looking on the Internet, I found a company that said they could provide that information for a $6.95 fee. For a bit more, I could get considerably more information, including e-mail and some personal background. Why not? I didn't know what I would do with the information, but it was intriguing to learn more about Ellen.

After I paid the fee, I had Ellen's address. What now? I continued my regular calls. Then late one afternoon, I decided I would try to find Ellen's house. As I'd suspected, it was at the beach. I parked just down the street, and I was a bit surprised by the size and prime location. How could someone in her line of work afford such a luxurious house by the ocean? There was obviously a lot I didn't know about Ellen.

I sat in the car feeling a bit foolish. What was I waiting for? What was I trying to find out? I wanted to see Ellen, but although I spent a couple of hours parked near the house, no one entered or left while I was there. I got a bit bored and drove home.

I continued my calls and began to park near Ellen's house every other day or so. It became a routine. One day as I sat in my car watching the house, I saw a woman and a man come out of the front door and drive off. I followed. They did some errands at stores in town and then drove into my neighborhood. Not just my neighborhood, but directly by my house. They did not stop but slowed down.

The next day, Ellen asked me several times what I was going to do on my birthday. I had forgotten that I told her the date. I said I didn't have any relatives or friends that I could ask over for dinner, so I had decided just to go to a nice restaurant for lunch and have a couple of glasses of wine in celebration. Ellen seemed very interested in the exact time I planned to go and when I expected to return. Too interested!

Rather than go to lunch on my birthday, I parked outside Ellen's house in my usual spot. Just before noon, Ellen and her friend (husband?) came out of the house with several boxes and put them into their car. I followed. After driving for a few minutes, I realized they were heading in the direction of my house. They drove into my driveway and took out the boxes, went to the front door, lifted the small statue I had next to the entrance, and picked up the key! They were breaking into my home! Why had I told Ellen about the key for the housekeeper?

I had trusted Ellen and now she was robbing my house. What a betrayal. I would fix them! I called 911 and told the officer a robbery was taking place. I gave my address and waited. A few minutes later, a police car pulled up next to mine. The officer got out and came around to the window. I quickly told him about Ellen and said that I thought she and her friend were robbing my house, perhaps trying to break into my safe. After showing him my identification and clearly proving that this was my house, the officer and his partner went up to my front door and opened it very carefully, their weapons drawn.

I walked up toward the front door waiting to hear shots. But what I heard instead were shouts of "Happy Birthday, Bob!" and then Ellen explaining to the police that she knew how lonely I was and had decided to throw me a surprise birthday party.

24. Water, Water Everywhere

I remember the exact moment I decided to kill him. I went into my uncle's study to ask for money to pay for a transatlantic trip with a group of my friends. I knew it would be a hard sell because even though he was very wealthy, he hated to part with money. And he particularly disliked giving me money. I worked in his bank as a minor functionary, and he gave me a small allowance. He was anything but generous. Actually, he was a skinflint who thought I needed to find my own way.

Without even a second thought, my uncle said he was not about to fund such a frivolous holiday. He also added that he had serious reservations about whether I should inherit his money given my total disregard for hard work and lack of initiative. I knew at that very moment what I was going to do. The question was not what to do, but how to do it without getting caught.

I waited patiently for the right situation. Then one evening as I was driving out of the estate, I saw my uncle standing on the dock by the lake located just out of sight of the house. An opportunity I could not pass up. I parked the car off the road and made my way through some trees to the lake. I had always been afraid of the lake, and water in general, because as a youngster I had fallen off the dock and was only saved from drowning by an alert gardener. Nevertheless, I steeled my resolve and walked silently up behind my uncle and pushed him into the water. He went down like a stone, and only a few bubbles came to the surface. That was all. The deed was done.

I immediately went to my club and made a point of leaving a trail of people who could swear I had been there all evening. I drank too much and after telling everyone I was not in shape to drive home, I spent the night there.

The next day, a gardener found my uncle's body in the lake and called the police, who in turn called me at the club. The following days and weeks were pretty much a blur. First a police inquiry, then the coroner's hearing; both concluded that the drowning was an accident. Then the reading of the will. Thank God he had not removed me as sole heir. And it was over, I got off scot-free.

After a decent interval, and rather quietly, I began to plan the transatlantic crossing that caused this series of events. I intended to enjoy every penny of my new wealth. I could not remember feeling so free and so optimistic about the future. I had many years ahead of me and the money to enjoy them to the hilt.

I went down to the White Star shipping line to book my trip. I asked for the best cabin on board, with all the perks. When in jest I mentioned my fear of water the agent said, "You are indeed fortunate, this is the maiden voyage of the unsinkable *HMS Titanic*."

25. Turkey Shoot

It seems like a weekly event. Some terrorist or unhinged person kills a bunch of innocent people. Trucks running down pedestrians, random shootings in crowded areas, and attacks on churches.

These incidents are always followed by an appeal from authorities to be alert and report anything that could possibly indicate someone, or some group, was planning an attack. I took that admonition seriously. First, I acquired a concealed carry permit. I regularly practiced my marksmanship at a local range. Then I began sharpening my observation skills. I watched people, studied their faces, and carefully observed them.

The internet was a great source of information, including techniques used by the Israelis and TSA to monitor people at airports. I found a good deal of literature on the subject; some of it contradictory. Psychologists tend to believe that there are no visible characteristics in appearance, dress, or behavior that would be a reliable indicator of a terrorists. But the Israelis and TSA have instituted systems to look for behavioral signs in potential terrorists. The TSA even has a list: exaggerated yawning, excessive complaints about security, throat clearing, staring eyes, whistling, and wringing hands. I decided to rely on the Israelis and TSA and assume that someone plotting an attack would exhibit some warning signs, some evidence of nerves.

I began to focus on individuals in markets, banks, and on the sidewalk. Once you start this process, it is interesting what you notice: people showing the full range of complex emotions—anger, frustration, happiness, and irritation. Watching their faces provided real insight into what they were thinking. It became a real game, and sometimes involved following a person around to "complete an observation."

One afternoon, I was conducting my reconnaissance at the shooting range while practicing my marksmanship. I noticed a middle-aged man in the firing position next to me. He had a particularly angry look on his face and was mumbling under his breath after each shot. He was intense; like he was killing something (or someone) with each shot.

We left the range at the same time, and I followed him into the gun store. While pretending to look at weapons for sale, I watched him purchase a dozen boxes of ammunition for different caliber weapons. Looking at his reflection in a mirror behind the cash register, he seemed wide-eyed and irritated. He was also perspiring heavily. The material I had read on what the Israelis and TSA looked for seemed more real to me. Was this guy going to commit some terrible act? I did not know, but the warning signs certainly were there.

I did not think I had enough evidence to call 911, but I was concerned enough to follow him when he left the range. He drove down Highway 1, turned west for a mile or so, and then turned into the parking lot of a small church. I watched him for a moment and then went into the church while he was getting something out of the trunk of his car. I greeted a few people in the church, but no one paid much attention. I fit into the congregation pretty well. I picked a spot close to the front in case I needed to take some action to stop what I believed might be a mass killing.

The fellow I had followed came in carrying a gun case for a long rifle. I took my revolver out of the holster and held it under my coat. He went to the front of the church and took a chair next to the small altar. He sat there very passively, but his eyes were staring at the congregation and he seemed to be repeating some words, as if rehearsing his lines.

The minister gave a short sermon and then turned to the man sitting next to him, indicating that "Jim" had something to say. I began to get really tense as Jim got to his feet and opened the gun case. I put my finger on the trigger.

Holding out the weapon, Jim said that he wanted to remind the congregation about the turkey shoot scheduled for the next day at the Findlay ranch on Route 60. He said he had bought the ammunition everyone said they needed, as well as prizes for the winning shooters.

To make things even worse for me, the sermon wasn't all that interesting.

26. Who's Got the Button?*

I had not been well, suffering a period of anxiety and tension over some recent failures, both personal and financial. I was in bad shape. My writing group had been canceled for more than a month for no good reason. My wife had put the nix on buying a much-desired Morgan sports car. Generally, I was in the doldrums; things were just not going great and, in fact, they were going downhill fast.

I decided I would visit a friend who years ago had been key to getting my life off the ground and getting me started after a bad patch. I called her and, after some confusion about who I was and why I wanted to visit after such a long period without any contact, she set a date that I eagerly anticipated.

She actually lived in a nearby town. I found my way to her house after a few mistaken turns and drove into her driveway. It was an unremarkable house but well kept. The most noticeable thing about it was several fluttering American flags and some posters in the windows indicating she had a son in the military.

I rang the doorbell and it was opened just a crack. A boy asked what

I wanted and when I told him who I was and that I was expected, he opened the door and led me into what I assumed was a parlor. After telling me that my friend had a doctor's appointment but would return in a minute or so, he sat opposite me and introduced himself as Nathaniel. Then without further comment he began telling me his story.

He said, "I am sure you saw the flags outside and noticed a number of pictures of a young man in uniform scattered around on various cabinets and tables. Those are pictures of your friend's son, who was recently killed in Afghanistan."

I was shocked and surprised because I did not know that she had a son, let alone that he had been killed. Nathaniel went on to explain that the son had died in a huge explosion and that the only thing they found of his remains was a button on a small piece of material from his uniform. He pointed at a table next to what I assumed was my friend's favorite chair. There, placed on a white piece of cloth, was a small military button, the only thing that remained of my friend's son. He talked about her turning the button around and around in her fingers and crying in sorrow over her dead son. Tears came into my eyes thinking about this tragedy and the impact it must have had.

Just then, my friend returned home and rushed to give me a hug. We had just exchanged greetings when the door opened again and in came a young man dressed in a military uniform. He was the spitting image of the young man in the pictures placed around the room. Before I could utter a word, he said, "Mom, I stopped by to have you sew on the button you found."

As I rushed headlong from the room, I was too upset to hear my friend say to Nathaniel, "I hope you didn't tell him one of your crazy stories."

The home they placed me in is quite nice. I made such a fuss that they cut all the buttons off my clothes. The doctors also indulge me by only wearing coats with zippers.

*Inspired by Saki.

27. The Caregiver

I went to the Memory Care Center very reluctantly but out of a sense of obligation. An old friend and neighbor ended up there after his wife could no longer care for him. It was not a depressing building—actually, it was new and clean, bright colors on the walls, plants scattered about, and happy workers.

Nevertheless, as I got off the elevator and the attendant unlocked the door of a large open room, my heart fell. There, scattered around in small groups, were a dozen or so people. A few sat alone, watching TV or just staring. All the patients—or nearly all—were old. I began thinking of them as inmates, not patients, although I knew that was wrong. Most had a rather vacant look, faces staring but not quite comprehending, mouths a bit gaping, dull eyes, but nearly all of them looked at me as if I had come to rescue them.

I wanted to get out of there immediately, but I had come to visit my friend and could not leave, at least not yet. The attendant led me to a corner where my friend sat. Dressed in a warm-up suit with big fuzzy slippers on his feet, he looked pretty good from a distance.

"You have a visitor, Kenny." I had known Kenny for 20 years, lived next door and consumed bottles of wine with him, played golf in the backyard, traveled to his hometown in New England, met his friends, attended various events involving his girl and my daughter. We were close friends, but he did not seem to recognize me. Continuing to look down with his eyes partially closed, he mumbled a few words I could not understand. What happened to the active, talkative, amusing person I knew?

I tried to engage him by telling stories of some of the things we did together, some of our silly adventures like the time we went into my hot tub and then outside to roll in the snow. I thought I saw a smile for a moment as if one of my stories had prompted a memory.

After an hour or so, I was worn out and decided it was time to leave. No, I had to leave! Kenny had fallen asleep and did not even know that I'd left. Poor Kenny. Poor Kenny!

The attendant took my hand as we walked out along a row of rooms, all with their doors open. As we passed one room a voice rang out,

"Sonny, you have come to visit me!" I looked in the door and there sat a large woman wearing a very strange gown. She told the attendant to bring me into her room. "It's about time my son came to visit."

I looked at the attendant hoping there was a way to escape, but she said, "Millie is a delightful lady, much more alert that most, and she would be excited to talk with someone. Her son has not visited in months, and she obviously thinks you are him." Reluctantly, I entered the room and began talking with Millie. She was interesting and began telling stories of what we did "when I was young," and how much fun I was growing up. She did not let me get a word in edgewise. She talked for an hour and finally I said I had to leave. The last thing she said was, "Come back soon."

I went back to see Kenny, but primarily to talk to Millie. Soon it became a regular thing in my life; nearly once a week I visited Millie and she told me more and more about my early life as her only child. It was a bit bizarre but interesting, and I did not have much else to keep my interest.

During one visit, Millie asked me to close the door to her room. She then came very close and, nearly whispering, said, "I need to tell you a secret. Just before I was put in here, I gathered a good deal of cash and jewelry together, put it in a metal box, and asked the gardener to bury it next to the water meter in my front yard. I wanted to have some independent means after my checking and savings accounts were taken over. I want you to go and dig up that box."

On my next visit to Millie, I met her son. He seemed unsure of me. He probably thought I was trying to scam some money from his mother. I called him the next day and told him about his mother's tale of the box of money hidden in the front yard of their old house. I suggested he go with me that evening to see if we could find the money.

That night, armed with a shovel, we parked a block away and walked to the house. It was easy to find the meter box and sure enough, there was the metal box under just a few inches of dirt. We took it back to my car and opened it with bated breath. The box was empty! The gardener must have taken the money before burying it next to the meter. On the verge of tears, Millie's son said that money would have helped keep his mother at the memory facility. Millie's son and I did not talk again. Nor did I return to the Memory Care Center to visit Millie.

I was too busy trying to figure out how to launder $100,000 in $1,000 bills and sell the jewelry from the box that I had dug up the day before Millie's son and I went to the house.

28. Uber Alles

Now when my wife and I travel, we frequently use the Uber car service. Even when we have our car, it seems convenient in an unfamiliar town or after a few adult beverages. I also began using Uber on my regular trips to Washington D.C. If the trips are longer than a couple of days, renting a car can be expensive, and it is not fun to drive in a crowded city and worry about parking and directions. So, Uber it is.

The last time I made the journey to D.C. it truly was an adventure, and Uber was the reason. I made several trips from my hotel during the first couple of days, all uneventful except on each of these trips the Uber driver was from the Middle East. Because I am interested in the area, I always engaged drivers in conversation about their country, politics, or religion. The first driver was from Algeria, and he was very talkative about his country. The second driver came from Iran.

When I asked why he came to the U.S., he said it was because he was Sufi and unwelcome in Iran. He gave me a long discourse on his religion. From the description of his family members in the U.S., it sounded like half of Iran had emigrated here and scattered throughout the country. The third driver was from Egypt and was very outspoken about the corruption and difficulty of an average person getting ahead in a country where "only the wealthy and connected people" have a chance. All in all, I learned a fair amount about the Middle East on these trips.

I needed Uber to get to a country club out in the Virginia suburbs. I used the app and indicated the destination. As you probably are aware, the Uber system knows where you are calling from, and broadcasts to Uber drivers that someone is looking for a ride. Someone in that area then indicates he is responding and the time of his arrival. His name and the type of car appears on your phone.

I waited outside my hotel for the driver but had not paid attention to the type of car that was coming to pick me up. A few minutes later, a car with "Uber" on the back window arrived. I got in, and off we went.

I did not pay much attention to where we were heading because I had never been to the country club where I was having dinner. After a half hour of winding through some country back roads, I began to look around and wonder where this club was located. As we were driving, I tried to engage the driver in conversation, but his responses were cryptic. He pulled into a deserted county park, turned to me with a small revolver in his hand and said, "Give me your wallet and your cell phone, and get out of the car."

I was not going to argue with him but asked how he thought he could get away with robbing an Uber customer? He said he was not an Uber employee; he had simply hacked into their system and found me before the real driver showed up. He said it was not useful to try and remember his license plate number because the plates were stolen. He then looked at me and asked if I had planned to give him a tip. A bit puzzled, I said I always gave the Uber drivers $5. He took $5 out of my wallet and gave it to me saying, "It's only fair to leave you with something." He then he looked in my wallet again and pulled out $1 and added it to the money he already had given me. "You were an especially considerate passenger," he said by way of explanation. Then looking at my wristwatch he said, "Take it off." Wishing me a good day, he drove off.

Not all rides with Uber are perfect and when I found my way back to the hotel, I intended to complain to Uber management if I could find a telephone with the appropriate app.

29. Murder for Dummies

The library box sat on a post next to the mailbox. It was about two feet long and one foot wide with a glass door hinged at the top. It held a couple dozen used paperback books. The number of books in the box at any given time varied with the season of the year. Lettering at the bottom of the box read "Take one, Leave one."

The library box was located on a sandy street with beautiful old canopy oaks that was popular with walkers, bikers, and people driving around the beach area. Many stopped to look at the book collection. Some took a book or two; some returned later with their contributions.

I checked the library at the end of the season. It was full. Obviously, people returning home from wintering at the beach were clearing their bookshelves. One book stood out because of its title and colorful cover. *Murder for Dummies* was done up in the same style as the well-known book series.

An enthusiastic mystery reader, I could not resist taking the book. I opened the cover, but I did not get past the title page because of what was written there in penciled script.

June,

This book only confirms my already strong feeling that we must act soon before events deny us the opportunity that we both feel is owed us.

Jim

For a moment I did not know what to think or do. Was this a serious message or simply a joke? What did "the opportunity" really mean? After thinking about this for a bit, I decided that I would follow the approach used by a private investigator in a series of mysteries I had been reading involving a character known as Maisie Dobbs. List the things that must be done to solve the problem.

What did I already know?

1. The book was placed in the box around May 1.
2. A local either on Sandfly Lane or nearby probably left the book.
3. If the inscription was as threatening as it seemed, I could not just sit by and ignore it.
4. The inscription seemed more likely to have been written by a friend or relative than a husband.
5. June might have been visiting Vero and may have been the person who put the book in the box.

What did I need to do?

1. Look at the books remaining in the library and see if any others had inscriptions indicating who put them in the box.
2. Read the book and find out how the murder was done.
3. Check local news for recent deaths.
4. Ask locals (Scribblers?) if they know of a family in the area with members named June, Jim, or James.

A quick look at the books in the library suggested several may have been put in at the same time. The books tended to be romantic novels and a couple of mysteries. None of these had inscriptions inside although the name—June—was written on the cover of one book, suggesting that she was a local or a visitor of a local.

I quickly read *Murder for Dummies*. The plot was simple: A rich aunt was murdered by her nephew and niece. The aunt died after "falling" inside her house. It was considered an accident by the police. There was no autopsy.

I decided to read all the local papers published over the past month to see if there were any deaths reported that matched the story in the book. I could not find anything that raised suspicion, although several elderly women had died in Vero during this period. There was no report of a woman dying from an accident in her home.

I talked to some of my friends who knew Vero Beach well and asked if they were aware of a Jim or June in the area. There were a couple of people named Jim, but no one could think of someone named June. I had run out of ideas and was getting a little tired of this mystery. I probably had let my imagination go a bit far, so I put the problem in the back of my mind.

A few days later, my wife and I were invited for cocktails by a couple that had just moved onto Sandfly Lane. We walked down the street to their house and were warmly greeted. There were several guests, including some neighbors and two of their old school friends. Talking to them over drinks, we discovered that they were from Chicago. Apparently, they were regular visitors with a relative in Riomar and had spent several weeks there in April. They had returned to Chicago afterward, but were back for the funeral of their aunt.

I had not caught their names when we were introduced, and I was now afraid to ask them to repeat it. But I did. Jim and June.

They were twins.

30. AlphaBay

With iPad in hand, I was sitting in my formless leather chair, my usual position early in the morning before my wife got out of bed. My chocolate Lab lay at my feet, occasionally trying to get my attention by licking my hand. Don't just sit there! Scratch my ears, you lazy bum.

I began looking at the morning news, scrolling through items without paying too much attention. And then there it was.

"The Department of Justice together with several international police forces has shut down two major Dark Web sites involved in selling drugs, arms, and other illegal transactions." More than 200,000 customers had been identified, according to the story. One of the companies was AlphaBay, owned by a Canadian man named Alexander Cazes. According to the article, Cazes had been arrested in Thailand and was later found dead in his cell.

My God was I rolled up in this net! Several years ago, a friend who lived in Canada recommended that I invest in a business one of his friends was setting up on the internet; a company that would offer some items not generally available. My first question was, "What kind of items?" I never got a specific answer, but a 30 percent return was expected. Compared to one or two percent offered by banks, I decided that ignorance of the "items" being sold probably would allow me to slip under any inquiry or investigation should it come to that.

Furthermore, I reasoned this was no different from an investment in a U.S. arms dealer—Northrop or Boeing. I was never asked to sign any documents and just needed to provide the money by cashier's check to an LLC at an address given during a telephone call. The company was AlphaBay, the same one involved in the recent international operation. I invested a fair amount of money and the promised significant return was met over the next several years. I had gotten much more back than I had invested. Hopefully, I was not going to get more than I bargained for.

I watched the news carefully as the investigation into these "dark sites" progressed. Interpol was tracking down customers who had purchased illegal goods. In that regard, I was clean. I had put money into the company but never bought anything. What was the likelihood that the authorities would track down investors? Maybe they would be more interested in who was running and financing these sites than customers who purchased drugs.

How well had I hidden my tracks? I had used cashier's checks that did not have my name on them. I assume the Feds could identify which bank had drawn up the checks. But I had paid for several checks in cash and stayed under the $10,000 amount that triggers federal interest. AlphaBay had sent my profits to a Bitcoin account that was encrypted and could not be traced to me. I had also declared my profits as winnings in gambling and a small inheritance. Somewhere in the AlphaBay records, there may be evidence of my transactions. But all in all, I felt reasonably safe.

Even though I believed I had covered my tracks well, I remained nervous. I suffered from heart problems over the past few years. My worry over the AlphaBay issue did not help with my health. As I followed the progress of the investigation, I had a few TIAs (mini-strokes) that were very worrisome. Those attacks only made me more concerned.

One morning, I was sitting at a table in the kitchen when I saw two men in suits walking up the driveway. My heart stopped for a moment. One of them opened his briefcase and took out a piece of paper. A summons? The doorbell rang. I could not move, and then I felt an intense pain in my chest. I went slowly to the door and opened it. The men saw my discomfort and quickly came in as I slumped to the floor. My last memory was reading the heading on the paper held in the hand of one of the men who was assisting me.

It read "Watchtower" announcing Jehovah's Kingdom with beautiful illustrations.

31. Character Assassin

She had been writing, and more importantly publishing, mystery novels for more than ten years. She was well enough established that her publisher called to ask how she was doing on the current book.

The principal, her only major character, was a tough and somewhat bent but not broken private investigator named Brad Singleton. He dominated each book she had written and had become a somewhat well-known fictional character, not quite the stature of Harry Bosch or Inspector Banks, but pretty close.

She was well along in her sixth book involving the adventures of Brad Singleton, and it was developing rather well. The plot was unfolding evenly with just enough surprises to keep it gripping. But Brad was being very aggressive, more so than she wanted. And then things seemed to change.

One of her author friends had mentioned the feeling of losing control of the plot when the book seemed to proceed along lines she had not planned. It was as if someone else had grabbed the plot and was moving it along outside her control. This was happening to her.

Things also began to happen to her in real life outside the plot of the book. It was as if someone had taken an active dislike to her and was acting out this hostility. A window was broken by a rock, and a favorite dress was slashed to shreds. She also had the strange feeling that Brad, the character in her book, was involved. It was as if he was objecting to the role that she was giving him in the story. How could that be? He was her creation and had no independent will. It became very disturbing, and she felt as though she had lost control of her own story line and consequently her life.

She began writing a chapter toward the end of the book. In the outline, a woman was alone in her house. The lights suddenly went out and Brad Singleton was supposed to apprehend a killer stalking the woman in the darkened house.

As she wrote, her computer, and then the entire house, went dark. She could hear footsteps on the stairs. The door to her study creaked opened, and she heard footsteps moving toward her. She recognized the aftershave lotion that her character Brad uses in each of her stories—Old Spice.

She yelled out, "Brad! Brad! Is that you?"

32. Pound Dog

I knew the moment I saw him that we were meant for each other. He seemed to sense it too as I peered through the wire cage. We both smiled. We needed each other.

The people at the pound agreed we were a good match—both of us had red hair and both of us were a bit loud. They completed the paperwork and the deal was done.

We got off to a pretty good start, although I had to show him where the water dish should be located and set the routine of feeding two times a day. He was more interested than I was in playing games, but I humored him. Both of us liked to take walks and ride in the convertible with the top down.

Life went on and we grew comfortable with each other. Pretty soon we adopted the same schedule and even some of the same habits, like sleeping late on Sunday mornings and then rushing out to see who could get the paper first.

I realized early on that a dog has a lot of responsibilities in the relationship with his "owner." (I never liked that term because I did not understand how a person could "own" me.) Dogs are expected to be "up" all the time, even when their owners are sick or suffering from a hangover. But dogs are expected to be out of the way when company comes and not smell people's crotches or pester the guest who does not like dogs.

That's a lot to remember.

33. Mistakes

I frequently paddle my canoe around the fill islands in the Indian River. Early one morning, I was circling one of the islands when I spotted something in the underbrush. Always a bit too curious, I decided to take a closer look. (Mistake #1)

Pushing my way through the bushes, I finally reached a blue and white ice cooler. I pulled it out into a small clearing and carefully opened it. (Mistake #2)

Inside were dozens of small brown blocks, each wrapped in plastic with a picture that looked something like a black widow. Drugs! I had several options: Leave the damn thing where I found it, turn it over to the police, or take it home. I decided to take it home after looking furtively around and paddling like mad back to where I left my car. (Mistake #3)

What to do with what looked like about 10 pounds of heroin wrapped in 2x4x5-inch blocks? Looking on the internet, I found that one pound was worth $90,000 – $120,000 on the street. How could I cash in on this without becoming involved with drug dealers? I knew I could not sell it on street corners or try to find a dealer without great risk. Taking either course of action would likely end up with the "owners" of the cooler coming to visit me with hostile intentions. I decided I would try to return the cooler to its owners and get some money for my good deed but protect my identity. (Mistake #4)

I thought the best course of action was to rent a mailbox at one of the local packaging stores using a false identity. Next, I put the following ad in a local newspaper. "If you would like the blue cooler and contents returned, please send a note indicating what it is worth to you—send to Alan, Box 22, UPS Store, Beachland, Vero Beach, FL 32963. (Mistake #5)

Days passed. I got no response from my ad and was getting increasingly worried. What if the drug dealers went to the UPS store and managed to get my name and address? I began to look around for suspicious cars in my neighborhood. Several days later, a black sedan went up and down my dead-end street several times and pulled into the driveway before backing out. They had found me! I panicked! That night, I put the cooler in the car and drove back toward the river. (Mistake #6)

As I drove down Route 1, a noticed that a car similar to the one I had seen on my street was following me. I stepped on the accelerator. The car behind me sped up as well, and I heard a siren and saw the flashing lights of a police car. I could not let the police find me with a cooler full of heroin, so I decided to run for it. (Mistake #7)

I was going too fast and lost control on the bridge at a curve just south of town. As I sailed over the railing, the last thing I felt was the cooler smashing into my head. The police report indicated that the driver died instantly from blunt force trauma. Police recovered the cooler and initially thought it contained drugs, but testing revealed that the blocks were a mixture of calcite and aragonite, two chemicals used in hydroponic agriculture.

Further investigation showed a label on the cooler that led them to Harbour Branch. A marine biologist there told them that as part of a project in the Indian River, he had taken a blue cooler filled with nutrients used in starting oyster beds and left it on one of the islands.

34. Never on Sunday

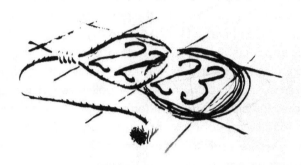

It was a sunny but cool Saturday morning, perfect for a hanging. The sheriff pulled on his long mustache and turned to his deputy, who stood next to him looking at the cowboy swinging by his neck below the scaffold. "You know, it was as if Jason was in a trance in the last hour or so before he was hanged." The deputy nodded but did not answer. Still dazed, he had never witnessed a hanging and it was not a pretty sight.

Jason heard none of this conversation, nor did he feel anything as his still body was lifted, the noose removed from around his neck, and he was dropped somewhat unceremoniously into the wooden coffin. If he had been alive, he would have asked himself, "What the hell happened? Where are my friends?"

He had spent the last couple of hours in his cell looking through the bars at the dusty street. He knew his partners in crime were coming to break him out of jail. That was their deal—those who escaped would come back and rescue anyone caught. It was the promise of brothers, not just braggart spinning. They had ridden together for more than a year and were like family.

He had no doubt he would be rescued, even as they put the hood over his head. He patiently waited for the shot to ring out and a coarse voice to cry out, "I think we will bring this necktie party to a halt!" He could imagine the hood being removed and his hands being freed. He listened for the sound of hoofbeats and the cries and shouts of those rough companions. All he heard, however, was the murmuring of the large crowd gathered to watch the hanging.

He heard a couple of children arguing about how much it would hurt to be hanged. Then he heard a click as the latch released the trap door under his feet. He was standing on air for a split second, and then fell to a sudden, painful, and deadly stop.

When the gang finally roared into town with guns a-blazing, they raced around the scaffold in the center of the empty square. One of the riders quickly rode over to a bench where an old-timer sat dozing in the sun. "You on the bench, where is the hanging?"

"You missed it, young man. It happened yesterday. Quite an event. The whole town was there."

One of the riders turned to the leader of the gang. "I told you they wouldn't have a hanging on the Sabbath. But you insisted that the paper indicated they would hang Jason on the 23rd. The calendar we have in the cabin is several years old. No wonder we got the day wrong! Are you sure the other date you circled on the calendar is actually when the mining payroll will be transported?"

35. A Person of Interest

I was not the most interesting person. In fact, I was rather boring and unremarkable. After a career as a laboratory technician working primarily with patient X-rays, I retired to a small town in Florida, living on a pension, social security, and some savings. I had received enough money from an inheritance to purchase a small but comfortable house. I kept myself busy reading, tending to a small flower and vegetable garden, and fishing. Fishing put me in touch with a group with common interests, and I enjoyed the casual friendship of those I regularly saw and talked to at various piers and docks along the river.

Early one evening, I was driving into town down the dusty road that led from my house. A young boy was walking along the road. It was some distance to the next house and several miles to town, so I pulled up alongside him and rolled down the window, asking if he would like a ride. He mumbled something but opened the door and hopped into the car. I tried to engage him in small talk and got a few terse answers, nothing of substance. I noticed that his hand—or more precisely, his knuckles—were bleeding and told him to get a Kleenex from the glove compartment. He grabbed a couple of sheets. When I asked how he had hurt his hand, he said something about cutting it on a barbed wire fence he had climbed over.

The young fellow requested to be let off at the entrance to a small park. I asked if he was sure he wanted to stop there because it was growing dark. He said he was meeting someone. I waited in my car for a while after the young man got out. I could see him standing near a picnic table. There was no one else around. I sat watching him for some time.

I do not regularly listen to the news or read the local paper. Instead, I get my information from the Wall Street Journal. Consequently, I did not know that a young boy had been found dead at a local park until I was talking with another fisherman along the bank of a nearby river the next day. Even then I did not connect this tragedy with the boy I had picked up along the road. He seemed fine when I left the park.

That connection became crystal clear when two men in suits knocked on my door. They identified themselves as detectives, showed me their credentials and asked if they could come in and talk to me. Although a bit apprehensive—as anyone would be if the police came to their door—I invited them in.

At first, they would not say what they were investigating, but eventually indicated it involved the suspicious death of a young boy. Apparently, someone reported seeing me letting the boy off at the park. Not many people lived on the road, and the car had been traced to me. They asked me what I had done the previous day. I described my activities as very routine. I had spent most of the day puttering around at home and then driving into town to do some grocery shopping in the early evening. When asked if anything happened during my drive into town, I told them about giving a young boy a ride to the park. They asked a number of questions about my exchange with the boy, when and exactly where I dropped him off. By this time, I was convinced that these detectives were investigating the death of the same young man.

My heart nearly stopped when they said it was necessary to take my car into the police garage to have it examined. They also asked me to give them the clothes I wore the day I picked him up. At this point I felt some panic and asked if I was suspected in the death of the youngster. They insisted this just an effort to follow up on some information they had received in their investigation. There were further questions about my trip into town, including what I bought and where, whom I talked to, and what I did after I returned home. They told me they would need to talk to me again and said not to leave the area. Under normal circumstances I would have been very concerned about the violent death of a young person, but I was more overwhelmed by what was happening to me.

I began reading the local paper to find out what was happening. There on the front page was a story that frightened me. Describing the murder of a young boy in a park, the story indicated that the police were investigating a "person of interest." There were few details, but it was clear I was that person. Over the next few days, the fact that I was considered a suspect in the murder became increasingly apparent. The police hauled me into the station for questioning on three occasions. First came the question of how a Kleenex with the boy's blood was found in my car. I explained that his hand was bleeding from a wound he said he got climbing over a barbed wire fence. The police wanted to know why I had not mentioned this before. I said I did not recall the incident until they mentioned finding blood. The detectives became very aggressive and told me to admit killing the boy. They said that if I came clean it would be better in the long run. At this point I asked for a lawyer, and further questioning was always in the presence of counsel.

The journalist following the story discovered the name of the "person of interest" and included it in every new story about the murder. I noticed more cars came by the house. Once early in the evening, one stopped. Some bottles were thrown, and someone shouted obscenities before driving off in a cloud of dust. People in stores where I shopped and at the local gas station treated me with hostility. I was isolated and friendless. More frustrating, how could I defend myself when already presumed guilty? This went on for weeks and then months. The police apparently had no leads and no other suspects. But neither the police nor the press would clear my name. Six months went by; six excruciating months.

Then one afternoon, two cars pulled into my driveway. The detectives that had interviewed me several times got out of the car. I was hopeful that at last they were going to tell me I was totally cleared and no longer a suspect.

When I opened the door, one detective said, "You need to come with us. Another young man has been murdered and a witness identified you as the person last seen with him."

36. Hate Mail

The letters began arriving just after January 1, as if they were part of a New Year's resolution. Every month a new missive came filled with criticism and nasty comments. They were short and direct. The comments were very personal and detailed my shortcomings and failings in no uncertain terms. Unfortunately, they were generally accurate. They also were mean-spirited and vindictive.

Initially, I thought the author was a crank who did not agree with some of the political comments I had made during one of my talks given to various groups around Vero, or someone who objected to my foreign policy pieces in a local weekly magazine. But after the first few letters, or perhaps better "notes," I realized that they were being penned by someone who knew me rather well.

Perhaps they were being sent by someone from my Washington past. I certainly had a few critics from a thirty-three-year career in intelligence. But it did not take long to figure out that the letters were being posted in Vero Beach. That certainly limited the pool of suspects.

I had talked to 30 or so groups over the past few years, and my articles got pretty good readership. Unless I was willing to go to the police and ask them to check the envelopes for fingerprints, that was too large of a population to focus on. Besides, some of the comments in the poison-pen letters seemed to come from someone who knew me well. That would eliminate most people who attended talks or read the *32063* newspaper.

I ran through the list of others who knew me well enough to make personal judgments and criticisms. My Scribblers writing group, an archaeology club, neighbors, several people at the morning market, and a few others. I mentally went through the list of people but could not come up with a likely suspect. I could imagine individuals offering some negative thoughts about me but could not think of anyone who would be so bitter as to write one note after another detailing my faults.

One Monday, I was returning from my weekly morning session at the Scribblers a bit early and stopped to pick up the mail. There it was, another letter from my detractor. I rushed inside to tell my wife about receiving another screed. I walked up behind her as she sat at her desk. She apparently did not hear me come in.

There on her desk was an envelope addressed to Dick Kerr at our address. She had already started the note. "Dick, you are such a dickhead."

37. The Wonderful Couple

They had rented a house in the older, more prestigious area of the island. They chose a well-known realtor and began looking at expensive homes, not the most expensive but in the seven-figure range. After settling on an older house, they spent a few hundred thousand dollars remodeling it. All this occurred about five years ago.

In the intervening years, the couple became well known in the upper-societal reaches of this somewhat snobbish town of wealthy sophisticates. They were a handsome couple, very presentable and well spoken. It seemed he had worked overseas, somewhere on the African continent, and had made a good deal of money. The rumor was that she came from a well-to-do family in England, maybe even a titled one. No one knew precisely, but some guessed she had gone to something like Bryn Mawr or Smith. He was believed to have been educated at a major English university, Oxford or was it Cambridge? The couple was never very specific about their past. But they were clearly "posh." Anyone with an English accent is always perceived as smarter than the typical American.

Both were brilliant conversationalists, clearly enjoyed the arts, and appreciated the finer things of life. Everyone envied their cleverness. It was difficult to find fault with them. They threw themselves into the social life, gave liberally to charities of the island, and even started a small foundation to give scholarships to disadvantaged students on the mainland. Noted for their charming dinner parties and regular attendance at all the best houses, the couple were generous hosts and sought-after guests. They were regularly featured in *32963*, the local weekly that reported on the comings and goings of the island elite. They had, as one of their admirers eloquently observed, "rainbows showin' out their arses."

A local reporter wanted to feature the couple in an article. They seemed a bit cold to the idea saying they really did not want that much attention. The reporter persevered. On the internet, she found a bit of information that led her to other sources. During her digging, it became clear there was more to the couple than people knew.

He had been a financial advisor to Qaddafi. Apparently, he had started working for a small financial firm as a gofer and moved up quickly into management. Reports about the firm and what happened to the Libyan dictator's money after his death was scarce. There were a few references in financial journals, but little in the way of specifics. Apparently, about $60 billion had been recovered, but another $40 billion or so was still missing. After Qaddafi's death, everyone associated with him and his money ran for the hills. The Libyan government and a variety of freelancers were trying to follow the money.

The reporter also uncovered more information. It turned out that he had gone to a small business school, not Oxford or Cambridge. She had no higher education. She was the daughter of a plumber, not a member of royalty or anything approaching it. In fact, neither had even reached A-level in schooling.

When the reporter returned to the couple to present her findings, they were hostile and wanted nothing further to do with her. When the story was published, the island community was abuzz. It did not take long before the invitations stopped coming and cold stares greeted them at various clubs and social settings.

They had not changed. They were still the same delightful, handsome couple. There was no evidence they had done anything illegal. But as one of the few couples who reluctantly continued to speak to them said, "We were disappointed because we thought you were one of us. It is not Qaddafi's money that offends us, but the fact that you misled everyone about your social status and education. How could you be so common?"

38. The Writers' Group

I have been writing a mystery novel for several years. It was going along swimmingly, with the characters well-developed and a plot that seemed to forge ahead effortlessly. I had really fallen in love with my work and believed that it could be a classic. I did not need help with my novel, and only joined the writers' group because I thought it would be interesting to see what others were creating. But the somewhat pushy members of the group insisted I read aloud some of the chapters I had written. Obviously, they wanted the opportunity to criticize my work. That was the beginning of the trouble.

The criticism flowed like wine: "Your dialogue is stilted; no one talks like that." "The story is listless and the characters match." "It is hard for a reader to believe that something worth reading is ahead." "You never stop using the passive voice, and yet your story supposedly is about action and violence."

And on and on, without a single favorable comment. At first, I thought that the group was just trying to be helpful and took their criticisms stoically. But after enduring several sessions of what at times was clearly ridicule, it became obvious that they enjoyed embarrassing me and making fun of my writing. They destroyed my confidence and wrecked my life.

I decided to get even. For the next session of the group, I wrote a bitter condemnation of their actions and, at the very end, described in detail what I was going to do to them in excruciating detail, and how each was going to suffer.

The police asked me to write this short description of what led up to the events that took place that Monday. They said I wrote well and had provided a complete and thorough description of that fateful day.

39. The Bickersons

The wife said, "I told you we should have been more careful when we picked out the site. But you said time was running out on the sale."
The husband replied, "You wanted a view on the hill."

"I told you I would be happier down by the grove of trees," she said.

He responded, "Wait a minute, you said you wanted to be near the children. I thought it was silly, because as soon as we got situated, they would move off to some distant area, and they now live hundreds of miles away—too far to visit regularly."

The discussion about the best location went on and on like it had for years. They just could not stop bickering. Over the fifty-odd years of their marriage, they had disputes over money, children, sex, relatives, furniture, and whether to paint the house and if so, what color it should be.

Their arguments were not hostile or even angry. They were just automatic. If he said it seemed warm outside, she would counter with, "I don't think it is as hot as yesterday." If she suggested going out to dinner, he would suggest ordering takeout.

Luckily, they did not talk about politics, because she was an unwavering liberal Democrat and he was an ultra-conservative Republican. They did not discuss religion, because she was a Christian Scientist and he was an Evangelist. Bringing up these topics could have permanently fractured their relationship.

The bickering had gone on so long that neither of them realized that they were doing it. Of course, their family and friends saw what went on, and most just ignored the back and forth, choosing to look at the positive side of their relationship. They lived together, if not in bliss, at least with affection and consideration.

Now side by side at the Hillsdale Cemetery, they continue their dialogue, undeterred by the fact that both have passed on. Fortunately, they had picked adjoining plots in that peaceful green area just north of where they spent their somewhat contentious lives.

They are still able to communicate with each other. The only things that had changed is the location and possibly the topics. No need to mention paint colors now.

40. Sounds of Terror

I remember the door of the prison cell closing behind me with a clang of metal on metal and an ominous click when the key turned in the lock. I remember the noise of the prisoners—coughing, praying, and at times, crying. The place was never quiet, always filled with muffled, agonizing noise.

But most of all, I remember the person who tortured me day in and day out. I was always blindfolded before he entered my cell. Your hearing is heightened to compensate for the loss of sight. I could hear him coming down the hallway of cells—the tapping of a cane at each step and a dragging foot. Tap-drag, tap-drag, tap-drag. He spoke to me only once, when he first entered my cell, saying, "I am a doctor, and I know how to inflict pain." From that point on, only his assistant spoke.

They wanted me to reveal the names of all the people in the resistance network. Each day, I sat and waited for him to walk down the hall. Tap-drag, tap-drag, tap-drag. At first, I was able to stand the pain and gave them only bits of information. But they were persistent, and I was weak. It was not long before I told them everything I knew. Ultimately, every time I heard him coming down the hall with his tapping cane and dragging foot, I cowered in the corner of my cell, sobbing—a broken man.

The prison was retaken by friendly forces, and I was sent to a hospital to recover. I had lost my sight either from physical or mental trauma, I had endless nightmares, and my nerves were shot. Months passed, and then a year. I thought I was slowly recovering.

One evening as I lay in bed, I heard it again. Tap-drag, tap-drag, tap-drag. There was no mistaking the sound. I began to scream and called out for help. A nurse immediately tried to calm me down. I replied, "The person with the cane and the dragging foot...he has come back to torture me."

She patted my hand and said, "Oh, don't worry, that's just our new doctor. He'll be taking care of you from now on."

They had to hold me down to administer the sedative.

41. Filibusters

"Filibusters," that is what the press called us, implying that we planned to engage in unauthorized warfare against a foreign country, similar to a revolution. In fact, we should have been labeled Freedom Fighters. There were about 20 of us. All former confederate soldiers, several noncommissioned officers. Many had served in the Cavalry. We were a restless group, unwilling to go back to our pre-war lives as merchants, farmers, and clerks. Five years of war had changed us and not for the better.

After the peace treaty was signed, a former Major gathered a few of us together and suggested that we were likely to be better off in this uncertain world if we kept our horses and weapons and stayed together. He also had a plan about going to Mexico to support some revolution underway there. He had fought in the Mexican War and had a Mexican town in mind. None of the rest of us had any plans or ties, so off we went, heading to Mexico. Freedom fighters! All for one, one for all.

We were not a gang of thieves or murderers, but we did a bit of foraging and liberated some stock and chickens along the way. We also appropriated a few horses for what turned out to be a long trip. We ran into some Southern and Union troops as we approached the Mexican border, but they were only interested in being demobilized and did not want to tangle with a well-armed and seemingly determined outfit. Besides, we were no threat to them. Our group worked well together—all for one, one for all.

Crossing the border at Shafter, we entered Chihuahua province and rode on to the city of the same name. The few Federalists in town were rounded up and sent on their way with instructions to tell their bosses a new regime had arrived. Not a shot was fired. The town seemed to welcome us. We did not demand much; a bit of food, some beer, and a friendly skirt.

Our Major put a solid government in place. Every man had an assignment in the town. I was responsible for relations with the community—complaints, requests, and demands. Things went rather well, and after a couple of weeks, we settled into a routine. This lasted for about a month. We knew it was too good to be true.

Sure enough, one day we were told by a new visitor that a large unit of Mexican troops was headed toward us. They clearly were not friendly visitors. They intended to retake the city, and they had the forces to do it.

After a hurried conference, we decided to save our skins and head back to the U.S. But we tarried a bit too long, and some of the Mexican troops had moved into position around the town as we made a break for it. Unfortunately, my horse was hit by a marksman as we raced through the main gate. The others made it to safety, but I was captured, and it was clear that the officer in charge of the Mexican troops intended to have me shot by a firing squad post-haste. My hands were bound, and I was tied to a pole in the city square. They apparently needed a bit of time to round up the half-dozen or so men required to hold a proper execution, so I was blindfolded and left alone in the square.

I was convinced that my friends would not abandon me. I could not see a thing, but I thought I heard horses, what seemed like muffled American voices, and the rattle of reins and people dismounting. Then I felt someone tug at the rope around my wrists. I was sure that footsteps around me indicated my rescue was underway.

Someone shouted "uno, dos, tres" and I heard the rifles fire and felt a crushing pain throughout my body. Then there was darkness.

"All for one, one for all."

42. Playing the Odds

No question that the elderly couple had thought about death and even talked about it on occasion. It was not unusual for people their age to worry about how difficult it would be to live alone after more than 60 years. Dying together seemed like a good option. They never considered suicide, but there was some mention of leaving this earth at the same time in a dramatic or catastrophic way. The specifics were always vague but being caught up in a shootout between police and robbers or some terrorist attack on an airplane was mentioned. Of course, the airplane incident would occur while on vacation or out of the country to avoid any involvement of family or friends.

In the meantime, they continued to live an interesting if not particularly exciting life. One of their favorite vacations was gambling in Las Vegas. They were drawn to the slot machines, although to many of their friends, the machines seemed terribly boring. On one trip, they had followed the usual practice of splitting up to find their favorite slots. He gravitated toward the poker machines because he thought they gave some free will to choose whether to draw cards. She preferred multiple bets on the penny slots that were more random. The only thing they could choose was the amount of the bet. She usually won, he usually lost over the course of several days.

He noticed her sitting at a machine with lights flashing the name of an old TV game show. He was amused to see how focused she was, intently looking at the screen and repeatedly pushing the "play" button. While he watched, she spilled her glass of free tonic water over the top of the machine and the lights began flashing "Grand Winner!" Bells rang and there was bedlam as people ran toward the excitement. He walked over to where she sat slumped over in her chair. As he reached down and put his hands on her shoulders, the 220 volts of electricity passed through his body as well.

Both died under the flashing neon sign that read, "You Bet Your Life." The prize was $500, the most either had won in years.

43. The Malicious Bear

It sat there staring at me—the birthday bear with its cold, impenetrable, dark beady eyes and black nose. On its right paw there was a button that when pushed caused the bear to sing the Happy Birthday song. It had a silly hat with a cluster of various-colored candles that lit up when it sang. My wife religiously phoned each child and grandchild in the family on their birthday and played the bear's song.

The bear was always around—staring at me, mocking me. Its white fur with the banner across its matted chest proclaimed—what else—Happy Birthday! I don't know why the bear tormented me, but I was determined to do away with it one way or the other. I did not trust the bear and its ever-pleasant demeanor. I always thought it held a grudge against me because I was not fond of birthdays. But it was more than that; the bear knew me too well. It understood all my foibles, watched everything I did and, although it said nothing, I knew it both pitied me and loathed me. I could see the disdain in its eyes.

I planned its demise as carefully as anything I had ever done. I waited with great patience for an opportunity to rid myself of that specter of evil. I knew I could just pull out its batteries and leave it speechless, but that still left the contemptuous look of disapproval, of contempt. No, I had to completely rid myself of the creature.

The opportunity came in a most fortuitous and convenient form. We were digging up the flagstones in the back yard. The workmen had left for the day, leaving one open hole ready to be covered by a flagstone upon their return. That night, I crept quietly into the room where my wife kept the creature. Thrusting it under my arm and careful not to touch the button on its left paw, I rushed into the yard. I could swear I felt the creature shivering, but I felt no remorse as I stuffed it into the hole in the patio. I only felt freedom as I shoveled a spade of dirt over the beast and placed the final flagstone.

The next day, my wife commented that I seemed to have a spring in my step. The creature was gone forever, and I smiled with contentment when I looked at the spot in the patio where it was entombed. I had never been happier.

One evening when my wife and I were sitting on the patio with another couple, the subject of birthdays came up. My wife asked me if I knew where the birthday bear was. I quickly tried to change the subject, but she forged ahead, telling the story of how she always called the children and grandchildren on their birthdays and played the bear's greeting.

Then we heard it! Very softly at first but increasing in volume—"Happy Birthday to you, Happy Birthday to You..." and on and on. Everyone looked down at one flagstone that seemed to be the source of the horrible greeting. I couldn't endure the singing and fell to my knees, clawing at the stone. As I finally lifted it, there looking at us was the birthday bear. I ran screaming from the yard.

I was committed to an institution the following week. On my birthday each year, my wife brings the bear and plays its song of cheer. The doctors still haven't figured out why I become so agitated when I see the cuddly creature.

44. The Fire

They sat around the dying fire unwilling to use more of the scarce wood. Most evenings, the small group of older men talked about the day, discussed what was planned for later, and told stories handed down from their fathers and grandfathers.

As in any group, there were a couple of men who took the lead and commented on what happened during their hunt—whose aim was on the mark and who consistently missed their target. There was some discussion about letting the man most skilled at sharpening and refurbishing points stay out of the hunt the next day. And finally, there was the usual back and forth about whether to have one of the group members spend so much time making scratches on bones and carving animals out of ivory. It meant one less person hunting for food, but it was argued that somehow the work seemed valuable.

Someone brought up the story that had been passed down from father to son, how many seasons ago their ancestors had hunted seals crossing wide stretches of water along the edge of the ice. They had lost the memory of where the tale originated but the story of the journey remained.

One of the men mentioned that a young boy digging in the bank of the nearby stream had uncovered a skull and brought it back to the camp. The skull was passed around the campfire for everyone to examine. Some thought it was a human, and one of the men speculated that because the skull was buried deep in the bank, it must have been there for many seasons. Perhaps a child belonging to a group living long ago.

The elder, a kind of shaman, said this talk was all nonsense. He said that he was with the first people that inhabited this site. It was not a human skull! It probably was that of an animal that no longer lived in the area. He told the man who was responsible for documenting the story of the visit to the site not to include any reference to the skull. The oral history must be amended, and that was that!

45. The Definition of a Psychopath

I noticed him the moment he walked into the funeral parlor. He was rugged-looking with a quick smile and muscular build. I should not have paid that much attention to him; after all, it was my father's funeral. But I could not keep my eyes off the man and as soon as I could manage it, I moved to sit next to him. It was a viewing, so there was no ceremony.

Consequently, I could talk to him without drawing too much attention. He was delightful, quick-witted, and interesting. Although I could tell he was successful by the way he talked and dressed, he did not talk about himself but engaged me in questions about my life, my concerns, and my views. I had never been so taken with someone so quickly.

We spent an hour talking and then when some relatives came up to me to offer condolences on the death of my father, he disappeared. I ran to the door to see if I could find him, but he was gone. I missed him almost more than I missed my late father.

For several days after my encounter with the mysterious man, I tried to find out who he was, but no one had any idea why he came to the viewing. I was devastated.

Several weeks later, my sister died under what some people thought were suspicious circumstances. There was a service for her and a viewing, just like the one for my father. I sat in the parlor near the casket and waited. I waited for several hours, but he did not show.

I was devastated once again.

46. A Fork in the Road

It is easy to criticize people for making the wrong choices: a politician who takes a watch as a gift or a private plane ride from a lobbyist, a town official who gets free tickets to the Rose Bowl. It is not hard to rationalize taking these perks. Many people feel they deserve some reward for the service they have provided. Others are tempted to avoid taxes or fees because the government already takes enough of our money. However, questionable decision-making can be a slippery slope.

What follows is a story of temptation and consequences. It all started when I decided to buy my son a mandolin for Christmas. My wife had a distant cousin who was a well-known craftsman of stringed instruments, and my oldest son had been learning to play a mandolin for several years. It seemed like a great match to get him a family-crafted gift; something that he would not buy himself but would appreciate forever.

I contacted the cousin who lived in Denmark and found that he would not have a mandolin available until June. I did not want to wait that long, and finally talked him into selling a very specially made model he used for display. It was a top-of-the-line instrument and even had been played by some well-known professionals. Very costly, but in for penny, in for a pound.

In what seemed like a great coincidence, I was scheduled to go to London the week before Christmas. Fortunately, the trip was on the company airplane and it would be that much easier to carry the instrument back to the U.S. I arranged for the mandolin to be delivered to my hotel in London by a special courier from Denmark. On my last day in London, the package arrived just before I was to leave, and I trundled off to the airplane with my present.

On the airplane, I talked to the pilot about customs in the U.S. Very subtle. On a previous trip, the customs official had come aboard the aircraft when we landed in the U.S. and collected the usual declarations of goods being brought into the country. But it was a very simple deal, and no one checked the baggage or even questioned us about what we were bringing back. I had paid a great deal of money for the mandolin and was thinking about saving a few hundred dollars on import duties by not declaring it.

The government did not need the money, or at least not my money. But there was some risk. If I was caught smuggling in something without paying duty, it could be embarrassing to me and the company and by having been a former Deputy Director of the CIA, it would make an enticing headline in the paper. At the same time, the risk of being caught seemed low. I thought about it most of the trip, weighing the options and considering the risk.

We arrived at Friendship Airport in Baltimore and sat on the runway for some time waiting for the customs official to come aboard the aircraft. I saw the vehicle pull up alongside the aircraft. I had to make my decision; was I going to declare the mandolin and pay the duty or just put down the few Christmas gifts I had bought in London and risk the outcome of discovery?

Always the cautious man, I chose to put the purchase on the customs form. But I was never billed. Honesty is the right answer.

47. Airport Revenge

I sat in the waiting room eating salted peanuts and looking around at the crowd. It was the usual mix of young and old, well-dressed and very casual, fat and thin—then one person caught my eye. I knew that man and disliked him in a visceral way.

He had bullied me, bad-mouthed my successes, argued against my promotions, and generally done everything he could to harass me. I could taste the bile rising in my throat and feel the perspiration beading on my forehead. If the crowd could smell hate, everyone would have been looking at me.

The plane was boarding, and I walked over to the TSA officer to casually point out my protagonist. "I don't want to be an alarmist or cause someone unnecessary problems, but I believe I saw a gun in that man's briefcase when he was getting his ticket out."

Boarding the plane, I saw several TSA officers escorting "my friend" to the offices in the back. As Homer wrote, "Revenge is far sweeter than honey."

48. The Dream

The dream was vivid, and I replayed it again and again in my mind. She was tall and strikingly beautiful. Her face was drawn in clear lines; a sharp nose, high cheekbones and a strong, chiseled chin. Certainly not a soft visage, but remarkably striking. Long auburn hair was piled up on her head like a pillbox hat. Even in short heels, she was approaching six foot. She was the complete package; a full figure and a wonderful, sexy Norwegian accent. Angela was her name. Wow!

I do not know where this dream took place, but it seemed to be at an inn along the sea. The dream apparently covered the period of a couple of erotic days, and I must have been considerably younger given my enthusiasm. We were having one last drink before parting. Angela whispered sweet nothings in my ear and said, "We must get together again, but you have to promise that you will help me." At this point I would have helped her do anything. I nodded. She said, "You must help me kill my husband." I awoke with a start. What a dream. I was exhausted.

Slowly, the details of the dream began to fade...all but the fact that I had agreed to kill her husband. My God, what was I thinking when I made such a commitment, even in a dream?

Several weeks later, my wife and I were invited to a party to welcome a family that had just purchased a house on our street. The party was hosted by the grand dame who provided the social glue for our social circle. As usual, we were introduced to the newcomers and made the rounds talking to neighbors. Suddenly, I came face to face with the woman from my dream, or my nightmare. "Angela." I nearly shouted out her name.

There was no question in my mind about who she was and as if to reinforce my memory, she said, "How good to see you again." With a slight smile on her face she added, "I am so pleased you remember my name and our adventure."

Then she motioned to her left. "Let me introduce you to my husband."

49. The Kidnapping

A Short Play

Four characters—three men and one woman

The three men are petty crooks who have decided to move into the big-time.

Lou—the leader of the gang. Middle-age, bald, stocky

Mike—short, worried, not too bright, mid-forties

Jim—Lou's nephew, mid-20s, good looking but often out of focus with weed

Mrs. James Sydney Knight—the kidnappee, late 30s, flighty, blond, tough

Background: Jim was one of Mrs. Knight's gardeners and had told Lou that her husband was rich, providing Lou with information about her daily schedule. The gang followed her car and grabbed her off the street.

The set: a large room with the men seated around a dining room table and Mrs. Knight tied up and gagged, sitting in a stuffed chair in the corner.

Lou: Well, I am glad that's over. It went well, except when she tried to bite Jim. Good job, Mike, in getting the plastic handcuffs and gag on so quickly.

Mike: She is a tough little broad. I have some scratches and a couple of bruises. I'm glad Jim was able to pin her arms and hold her while I got the cuffs and gag on.

Jim: Now what do we do?

Lou: I'm going to call her husband using the disposable phone. (dialing) Mr. Knight, we have kidnapped your wife and are holding her for ransom. $200,000 dollars in small bills. Do not call the police. I'll phone you in three hours with instructions on how to deliver the money.

Mike: How will he know that we really kidnapped his wife?

Lou: Why do you think we had her leave a message on her phone saying she had been grabbed off the street and was being held for money? He'll call her phone and get the message.

Mrs. Knight: (muffled noises from the corner)

(three hours later)

Lou: (dialing phone) Mr. Knight. Do you have the money? What do you mean you're not going to give us any money? You don't want her back? Don't you understand that we have your wife? You can't mean that! Dump her into the nearest swamp? What do you mean we would have to pay you if we brought her back?

(Hangs up.)

Lou: He doesn't want her back. In fact, he doesn't care what happens to her. What do we do now?

Mrs. Knight: (muffled noises increase)

(Lou removes gag.)

Mrs. Knight: You bastards! Keeping that gag in my mouth for hours. Get me a glass of water and cut these stupid plastic cuffs off. Untie my feet! I am so pissed off at you for roughing me up. The only thing that makes me angrier is my husband. What does he mean he won't pay to get me back? Throw me in a swamp? I'll teach him a thing or two...

(Jim runs off to get a glass of water. The other two men stand and stare at Mrs. Knight, totally intimidated.)

Mrs. Knight: You had a recorder on when my husband said he didn't want me back and said you should throw me into a swamp, didn't you? Play it back.

Mrs. Knight: (Listening to the tape recording of her husband.) One of you is going to drive me back to my car. I'm going to check into a hotel and call a divorce lawyer. Give me the tape recorder and before I leave, I want your names and telephone numbers. I may need you to convince my husband that I mean business. This should be worth millions, and I'll make sure you're paid something even though you should go to jail for grabbing me off the street.

(Mrs. Knight and Jim leave.)

Lou (looking at Mike): This kidnapping business is tougher than I thought. Maybe we should go back to burglary.

PART III
TWILIGHT

Intelligence officers, analysts, and operators alike are often faced with situations that defy calculated logic. Despite the abundance of intel collected from previous outcomes, when faced with unexpected circumstances or a lack of reliable information, a resolution can be frustratingly elusive. We all know that everything can be explained if properly investigated, right? Every question has a logical answer. Or does it?

50. The Ugly Truth

He was a short, stubby man with a narrow, pointed nose. His personality was as stunted as his physical makeup. He was incapable of holding a normal conversation, or even exchanging simple information.

Hygiene was another problem. He smelled and had bad breath. His hair looked like patches of fur were glued on his head. He had no eyebrows and a thin mustache. He stuttered. What a mess!

Nevertheless, I was forced into a weekly conversation with this rather unpleasant and uninteresting individual. I had to tell him what I had been doing and if I had been following the rules laid down for me. He pried into my personal life and seemed intent on embarrassing me.

How had this man ever become a psychiatrist?

51. They Are All Around Us

Shortly after moving to a home on Sandfly Lane, I was invited by Gertrude Terry to join a writing group called the Sandfly Scribblers. I believe she thought I was an acceptable candidate for this rather elite clique after she attended a talk I gave at her church.

She could not have known much about me, and I could have been a serial killer or a real crack pot. Or I could have been an extra-terrestrial disguised as a reasonably normal person.

I began to attend the Monday morning sessions, bringing either short stories on the somewhat strange side or articles commenting on foreign policy that bore on my supposed area of expertise. The group was a mixed bag—it numbered up to ten people, but normally about eight showed up. They wrote memoirs, biographies, short fiction, and other miscellaneous genres.

I have long had an interest in extra-terrestrial presence on earth. I believe —no, I know—that aliens invade people, putting the real person in a sort of limbo while they assume their life. They slip out when they are ready to move on, and the real person returns with no memory of what happened during their leave of absence.

I do not know how many of these aliens there are living in our communities and learning about life on this planet and reporting back to "their" people, but the number is significant.

I began to suspect that one of the Scribblers must be an invader, but which one? I watched each of them for a telltale sign. Studying their expressions and reactions to various situations became a serious task. They were a diverse group and tended to hold in their emotions. One claimed to be from Ireland. A couple of others were originally from New York and always reminded us that they really liked the city. Very suspicious. Most of the others had deep roots in Vero. But backgrounds mean little unless the "alien" forgot their individual legend.

I thought the writing might give them away: A book about an Ice Age dig, recollections from a farm in Ireland, a story about life and failed marriages, tales that were never quite finished concerning dinner parties and confused women, a book about the memories of a childhood home, and stores of adolescence. All were interesting but not revealing. Their gestures and language did not help, although all had certain odd habits and mannerisms. I could not clearly identify the alien, if there was one in our midst.

One member of the group kept notes and organized outings but did not often write. I have some suspicions about her, but they have yet to be confirmed. I will have to leave the identification to the rest of the group because I have been called back to my home planet, and a transporter is picking me up soon. The "normal" and less interesting Dick Kerr will return. No doubt some will notice a falling off in the quality of his writing.

52. Haiku

Shamota was a lecturer at the University of Tokyo before entering the Army. He taught poetry and was partial to Haiku. Of course, that was before the war and years ago, but he still loved poetry and spent hours writing at night.

His Army job was about as far removed from the university as one could imagine. He was the officer in charge of a prisoner of war camp in the Philippines, a place that housed about 500 U.S. soldiers captured at Corregidor.

Shamota came from an ancient family that had deep cultural roots. He had little sympathy for his captives. His attitude toward the U.S. was one of contempt; it was a country that had no history, no real culture; one that was populated by those refuse from other nations—mongrels. As an experiment, he decided to select three officers from among his prisoners and educate them. God knows they needed it. He explained the fundamentals of Haiku to the perplexed trio and gave them the task of creating poems.

The next day, he reviewed the three poems.

1. cruel bastard	2. no matter what	3. no forgiveness

tortures and starves
    without sympathy
	our will is strong
	    we will not break
		for your crimes
		    your soul is dead

He was angry and insulted. Clearly, they did not understand Haiku structure and were as unsophisticated as he thought. He told them that Haiku expressed happiness, pleasure, and nature. They ignored his instructions, but he would not give up. He would punish them and then give them additional lessons in the beauty of Haiku.

wind softly blowing
leaves scattering randomly
rattling on the ground

53. Returning

The boat was pushed up on the sand by small, insistent waves. He sat very still, facing the sea, holding the oars in his hands. The boat shook slightly as the waves pushed it higher on the flat beach. He still did not move even though a darkening sky suggested rain. A somewhat larger wave caused the boat to turn sideways and, looking a bit startled, he finally began to climb out onto the sand. He nearly fell but grabbed the gunwale and managed to get his bearings without falling. He stumbled away from the boat without looking back.

He made his way toward a clump of trees, walking slowly, with the uncertain steps of an old man. Dressed in casual clothes and wearing a windbreaker, he looked presentable, but a bit worn around the edges. What was he doing there all alone on this sandy shore?

He certainly did not know where he was or how he got there. He remembered the story of dead or dying souls crossing the river Styx with a boatman carrying a scythe. He had arrived without an escort. Besides, behind him was a sea, not a river. Was that a good sign?

He looked around and had a sense that he had come this way before, but when, and why? He walked carefully up the slight slope and then saw what appeared to be an old stone walkway with steps leading up the hill. It seemed familiar.

He remembered his mother reading from an old diary about a great-grandfather who was the bane of the family. He apparently was a difficult man who made quite a bit of money but was a notorious cheapskate. He never helped his less successful family members. When he died, he was buried not in the family plot but on an island in the bay, sent to his maker with little fanfare and even less friends.

As he recalled the story told by his mother, he wondered if this could be the island. The more he thought about it, the less enthused he was about climbing the steps, but he did not seem to have a clear alternative. He trudged up the path and soon reached the top of a slight hill overlooking the bay. Sitting on a step, he looked back at the darkening sea and wondered what he was doing there.

Off to his right and nearly covered in vines were what appeared to be several graves. Clearly no one was taking care of the plots; they were heavily overgrown. He moved over to a headstone and after brushing vines away, he read the name and date: Michael McPherson, born January 1865, died April 1930. He could see the words etched into the stone: "He was a selfish, hard man, uncompromising and stubborn to the end."

He moved to another marker and it read his own name, Michael S. McPherson, born in October 1935. The date of death was obscure; it was growing too dark. However, the same harsh inscription could be seen on the second stone.

He did not know if he was looking into the past or to the future. But he did know those words were an apt description of him. Could he go back and change that judgment?

It was too late. He had crossed over.

54. The iPad

I used the iPad for all the questions I've had in life. Any question that popped into my mind could be answered in just seconds by that magic device. Surely there was no end to the knowledge that it possessed.

"Who sang the song, 'What Ever Happened to Randolph Scott?'"

"When was Jerusalem sacked by the Crusaders?"

"What is the telephone number of the closest Italian restaurant?"

"How do I get to Indian Town?"

It never failed to produce an answer or at the very least lead me in the direction of an answer. What were its limits? Could it give information about the future as well as the present and past?

If the questions were analytic, such as "How long will it be before (a particular place on the earth) runs out of water?" or "When will the next earthquake occur in Los Angeles?" the device could provide an answer based on probability or estimates.

Could it produce personal information about incidents, successes, life forecasts, deaths? For example, what if you asked it whether you would likely suffer from some disease such as cancer or a heart attack? In fact, it could provide data on such events based on your current health, diet, and exercise regime. It obviously could help with information on investing and the chances of profit or loss. Was gold a good investment? You could get several different views with enough information to let you determine whether it was a good idea.

I decided that the key questions would be, "How long will I live?" and "What will cause my death?" A bit morbid, but interesting. The computer came up with some useful information about the likelihood of contracting a disease and the life expectancy of someone my age and physical condition. This information was interesting but not good enough—I had asked for specifics. Exactly when would I die and under what circumstances?

I phrased the question any number of ways, but no answer was forthcoming. I could find the obituaries of others with the same name, but the future was unclear. Technology had failed me, and I would die without knowing the details in advance. What good is the iPad if you cannot peer into the future?

55. Bad Little Boy

He was a bad little boy, but he had convinced nearly everyone that he was "a perfect angel." He had figured out how to con people using polite manners and engaging in adult conversation.

Beneath that façade was an ugly and evil core. All his peers knew that he lied, played nasty tricks, and managed to place blame for his actions on others. He could fall into a pit of manure and come up smelling like a rose. Butter would not melt in his mouth. A nasty piece of work.

• Look at him standing there with a smile on his face as he tells the biggest lies.

• Watch him point his finger at others, blaming them for things everyone knows he did.

• Listen to him promising to do better and change his evil ways.

• Even when he hugs you, it's phony.

He will make a great politician one day.

56. Mirror Image

I always wondered if there was someone in the world who looked and acted exactly like me. A double! Out of the billions of people on earth, wasn't it possible that just one or maybe two would resemble me? Wouldn't it be fascinating to walk into a store or a bar and see a mirror image of yourself? Could he have a wife named Jan and four children and nine grandchildren? No! That would be expecting too much.

I didn't take the idea seriously until things began to happen that got me thinking about the coincidence of two people looking and acting alike. It started with a friend saying he enjoyed talking to me at the party and was a bit surprised to hear I had been an early supporter of the president. Apparently, I was the life of the party, talking about the election, telling jokes, and amusing the crowd.

I had not been to a party recently, and I would hardly be considered a highlight at most soirees. I soon forgot the incident, thinking that my friend was just a bit muddled.

A few days later, I went to the Monday morning gatherings of the Sandfly Scribblers, a local writers' group. At the meeting, there was some discussion of how much they enjoyed the story I read at the previous Monday meeting. I did not attend that meeting; I was in London. What was going on?

I got another shock when the retired head of a military organization called to thank me for the wonderful speech that I had given. He said his group was abuzz with praise and wanted him to make sure I was invited back. I had not left the house last night.

Even my oldest son commented on how much he appreciated a recent conversation discussing some of his concerns. I could not remember any such session. I was getting worried, no, terrified. What was happening?

The final blow came when I arrived home after an appointment. As I stood on the porch peering through the screen door, my chocolate Lab growled at me without any sign of recognition. But more startling, I saw my double sitting in my favorite chair talking to Jan. They were having an animated conversation, and he reached over and put his hand on hers. She responded with a smile and a laugh.

My double was pushing me out of my life and he was more likable, smarter, and cleverer that I ever was. Damn him!

57. From the Grave

Norris Edington was my best friend from grade school until his death a few years ago. We first met when we were neighbors in a little logging town in Oregon. We ran around together, playing baseball, shooting keepsies marbles, walking the log ponds, riding around with abandon on our bicycles, and just wasting time. His father was a bit of a drinker and would send us to the bar just across the railroad tracks from our neighborhood for a bucket of beer. On occasion, his mother would order us to the bar to guide home a somewhat unsteady and difficult drunk.

I moved to another town, and Norris and I did not see each other again for several years, until we started college after a tour in the military. We picked up our friendship in college, and it continued off and on for the next forty years.

I ended up in a government job in Washington, D.C., and Norris, who was an engineer, went to work for a large oil company, spending much of his time in Africa. He never married and often turned up unannounced at Thanksgiving and Christmas looking for a home-cooked meal and familiar company. He paraphrased an old Bulgarian proverb, saying once you invite a friend for a Christmas dinner, you are forever obligated to give him meals.

Norris and I had endless discussions about politics and religion. He was something of a mystic and often talked about life after death and reincarnation. He was convinced that the spirit or the soul or something lived on after the body died and speculated that perhaps humans were reincarnated in the form of animals and birds. I was skeptical but humored him.

At one point in our relationship, probably over a few drinks late in the evening, we agreed that the first one of us to die would try to communicate with the other. An easy concept to agree upon, but seemingly difficult to implement.

Several years ago, I was sitting by myself in the sunshine just thinking about "things" when I felt a strong chill as if a cloud had suddenly blocked the sunlight and a draft of cold wind rushed over me. I felt something ominous had happened but had no idea what. A few days later, I learned that Norris had died in Nigeria where he was working. I found out later that the time of his death coincided with my episode on the lawn. I remembered our pact and shivered. Would Norris try to contact me?

He was always fascinated with certain animals—owls and dogs, for example. There are large oak trees behind my house in Florida, and one evening, two dark owls sat on one of the limbs hoo-ing at one another. "Hoo!" I called out … and they answered. I rushed into the center of the yard and said, "Norris, is that you?" The owls flew off, and I stood there somewhat embarrassed about what I had done.

I began to talk to dogs, thinking Norris might have assumed their form, but only the ones born after Norris' death. I tried to talk with them when their owners were not paying attention. I would softly say, "Norris, Norris, can you hear me?" I never got an answer, but sometimes the dogs would look at me with particularly interested expressions.

I was even more careful about stepping on insects after my friend's death, although I did not know how to communicate with them.

The contact from Norris came as a surprise. It was a message from the grave, and it came in the form of the following e-mail:

"Greetings from Nigeria"

No. 7 Mambilla Street, off Aso Drive

Maitama District Abuja Nigeria

Direct Telephone Number: (+234 -81-535-117-07)

ATTENTION: BENEFICIARY

Congratulation for you are to be paid $5,000,000 as the heir of Norris Edington

Etc., etc., etc.

58. A New Civilization

The project to colonize a distant planet was in its final stage. Buildings, food and all the necessities for a permanent site on the distant sphere had been sent by unmanned transporters over the past several years. What remained was to identify the people who would settle this new world. No small task.

The government set up a special commission to select about a dozen people to make the voyage and build this outpost in space. The commission included physicians, psychologists, sociologists, politicians, astronauts, religious leaders, historians, and representatives of all ethnic and social groups in the nation. Everyone wanted a say in what could be the founding of a new civilization. Everyone wanted their group represented, although all agreed that a principal objective was to avoid transplanting the civil, religious, and ethnic strife that had so dominated earth since the beginning of time.

A decision was made by the commission to choose people with high IQs and those free of major disease with good family medical histories. While there was to be ethnic and religious diversity, every effort was made to avoid individuals who were outspoken advocates. Radicals and extremists were rejected.

A varied skill mix was sought with near equal emphasis on conceptional and mechanical ability. There was an equal division between men and women, and after considerable debate, it was decided that women must be of child-bearing age and no gays would be selected—this group was needed to create a new civilization. The ACLU was not pleased. At first there was an attempt to get one male and one female of each major religion and ethnic group. But those involved in the selection process became convinced that religion played too strong an influence in conflict and decided to emphasize the selection of agnostics and nonbelievers.

The selection process was rigorous as every attempt was made to find people who were not judgmental and had no strong views about what others did or believed. The group was carefully monitored, and anyone too outspoken or argumentative was left out.

Some members of the selection committee began to worry that no natural leaders seemed to stand out and that individually, the selectees were boring and unremarkable. But the consensus was that they were creating a conflict-free community, the first of its kind in history. And the group got along remarkably well, with little or no friction even during periods of considerable stress.

The date for launching the transporter with this remarkable crew grew closer and closer and everything seemed to be progressing swimmingly. But there was one festering problem the planners did not foresee.

One of those selected was having grave concerns about the entire project. He had gone along with what he considered "brainwashing" because he believed in the necessity of building a new community in space. But he was increasingly worried that the creation of a community without values and beliefs would produce disastrous results. In his view, an amoral civilization would lack creativity and stifle that which made life most meaningful. The absence of belief in God or some "first cause" and a set of principles that provided direction in life could leave the new civilization without any recourse when faced with overwhelming crises. There must be something greater than the individual to provide meaning to life. Also, without some conflict, how would new ideas develop? Who would provide the music and poetry?

He knew he could not raise his concerns with the selection commission because it would only lead to his being kicked out of the group. He had to change the outcome somehow, but if he did something before the launch, it would just delay the project for a short time.

The solution could be simple but dramatic. A capsule of some type of poison gas—cyanide perhaps—in the air system of the transport during the actual trip. But that would mean killing innocent, if useless, people including himself. It would also be against his fundamental beliefs.

Perhaps a more effective solution would be to bring God with him and convince others about the "correctness" of his position. What he needed was a "sign" during the long trip: A sign that would convince others their fate was not just the result of their own actions but a gift to them from a higher authority.

The date of the launch was fast-approaching. Then there was a dramatic turn of events. When the materials were sent to prepare the site for human occupancy, a variety of sensors were put in place including video and electronic monitors. Recently, these devices showed something or someone setting things up. Boxes were being opened, equipment turned on and movement could be detected. It would take weeks for the video to be transmitted.

What would it reveal? Had some other earthlings beaten them to it, or was it aliens from still another planet?

They would have to wait and see.

59. No Legend

It had been a dream-filled night of fleeting images, bizarre events, and swirling nightmares. I opened my eyes with some trepidation. I don't know why, but I was afraid. Looking around the room, I saw a chest of drawers with what appeared to be family pictures and a large accumulation of knickknacks scattered on every shelf. There was a woman in the bed with me, covered to the tip of her grey hair in blankets even though the morning was quite warm. I had no idea where I was or the identity of my bedmate.

Getting up quietly, I made my way to the bathroom and put on the shorts and T-shirt that lay on the counter. An old man stared back at me from the large bathroom mirror. I did not recognize him—wrinkled, grey-haired, tall, and overweight. I found a driver's license in the wallet in the back pocket of the shorts and recognized the picture as the man in the mirror. The name was not familiar, however.

Wandering around the rather large house, it became obvious that whoever lived here led a somewhat chaotic life. The furnishings were a mish-mash, the walls were covered with a variety of paintings, photos, and "stuff." There were strange objects scattered around. The patio was piled with mismatched furniture.

I sat down in the large, wrinkled chair in what I assumed was the living room and tried to figure out what was going on and how I fit into all this. Nothing I saw in the house was familiar. Picking up a magazine, I found I could read the stories.

The large brown dog at my feet seemed to know me. What was I going to say and do when the woman in the bedroom got up, came into the living room, and saw me sitting there? Would she scream or was I a fixture in her life? I waited patiently.

She walked into the room, asked how I slept and began scrolling through her iPhone. I found that if I just asked questions and agreed with everything she said, it went well.

"What are your plans today?"

"What would you like for dinner? Shall we go out or bring something home?"

"Yes, I will take out the garbage."

It was surprisingly easy to carry on without having a clue about my past. I knew how to read and write and found I could function in the kitchen and even drive. Fitting into my "old" schedule was more difficult. When asked if I was going to something called the Scribblers—apparently a writing group—I begged off, blaming the flu. I also canceled some speaking engagements, claiming I was having memory issues. An understatement.

After a week or so of trying to adjust to my new circumstances, I sat down and seriously considered my situation. I realized I was a totally new person. I had no biases, no prejudices, and no opinions. I was not judgmental, and I found that when people at social gatherings asked my opinion on a subject, they seem genuinely more engaged when I responded by asking them what they thought. My wife (I discovered her name was Jan) commented one evening over drinks at how pleased she was that I no longer told those endless stories or anecdotes from my past and instead listened to what others had to say.

The most interesting and at the same time most worrisome thing was that despite a totally blank mind, I seemed to get along quite well with everyone. They seemed to like me in my present condition even better than my old self, back apparently when I was argumentative, difficult, opinionated, outspoken, and at times, rude. I had become nicer and far more tolerant according to some of the comments I heard.

Then why did I feel exactly the same?

60. The Death Clock

Most people think about death. It is natural to either worry or just be curious. I am no exception. When will it happen and under what circumstances? What kind of experience will it be? Painful and frightening or peaceful and serene? I don't think I was unduly concerned about dying until I saw a site on the internet called "Death Clock" which predicts the exact day, hour, and second of your death based on personal information you provide.

I submitted the requested information. The Death Clock predicted that I would die on June 11, 2022. Seven years from now. More precisely, it gave me 2,715 days, 21 hours, 24 minutes, and 43 seconds of life remaining.

My first reaction was to shrug off this prediction as another wild guess like those offered by the fortunetellers at Cassadaga. But then I began to worry—what if the prediction was right? How would it change my life, my way of thinking, my actions?

Initially, seven years seemed like a long time. But looking back, it actually was very short. As the minutes ticked by, I began to panic. My life was slipping away like water through my fingers. Should I plan my days more strategically and fill them more thoughtfully? Should I examine my bucket list of things I want to see or places I want to visit? Should I finish my autobiography? Should I stop going to committee meetings discussing Vero Man? Should I spend more time with my wife? Less time? Should I write more or write less?

I could not answer any of these questions. All I could do was watch the clock and look at the calendar and despise the internet.

61. The Pandemic

The pandemic of Ebola in the U.S. began at precisely 0900 on July 1, 2015, when the United Airlines flight UA-12 landed in New York. A young Liberian student got off that plane. He had left Monrovia, Liberia the previous day taking a flight to Pretoria in South Africa where he boarded United to the U.S.

During the trip he asked the attendant for an aspirin, hoping it would help his headache. He thought he might be coming down with a cold. He had a cough, but it did not seem serious. He had no idea that he was carrying a new strain of the Ebola virus, one transmitted not by contact with body fluids but by aerosol—coughing.

After going through customs and showing his temporary student visa, he boarded a plane for Atlanta where he had family. During his travel, he had infected several passengers boarding flights to South Africa and the U.S., and further spread the disease on his way to Atlanta.

He was met at the Atlanta airport by several cousins. All of them happily embraced their relative from Africa. He stayed with a large family that had children ranging in age from 7 to 15. Consequently, he infected a grade school, intermediate school, and high school. Unbeknownst to him, he was spreading the deadly virus faster than a weapon of mass destruction.

Within a week of his arrival in the U.S., the number of people exposed to this new and virulent strain of Ebola was in the hundreds; it soon would be in the thousands.

No one in the U.S. health system had any idea that a new disease had been let loose in the country. No one had yet gone to a doctor or a hospital seeking treatment.

No one knew if they were a carrier.

62. Off to Never-Never Land

The Sandfly Scribblers enthusiastically supported the idea of an overnight trip to Cassadaga. The town is a haven—perhaps better a coven—for those interested in spiritualism. Several members of the writing group clearly were experienced spiritualists or at least had attended séances or other unexplained phenomena. It seemed like a harmless and perhaps amusing trip.

I began to have second thoughts after a quick look at the various web pages connected with the town suggested that it was full of scams. Then deeper thought about the various offerings raised some interesting questions about whether it was wise for a group already susceptible to weird thoughts and strong bouts of imagination to open itself to further craziness and erratic thoughts.

What if one of the more vulnerable members of the group fell victim to some wild idea about life after death and decided to move immediately into the next life? What if one of them decided to enter the ether world of the past or the future and was unable to return? What if secrets were exposed that ended friendships or marriages, or fundamentally changed the relations among the group? What if control passed from individuals to some stronger force?

This may all sound silly and probably should be of no concern to serious folk, but lives have been ruined by misguided counseling and interventions by friends and relatives. How much more damage could be done by evil spirits on the impressionable minds of the vulnerable Sandfly Scribblers—a group that is already on the threshold of losing its grip on reality?

This trip could nudge them over the precarious edge.

63. Step into the Twilight Zone with Siri

Beth and Alex had just finished shopping at Publix and were packing the groceries in their car. The receipt indicated they had just saved $10, something that always baffled the couple seeing that they paid about $100 for the lot.

Alex started the engine and the navigation system announced it was on. Siri said, "We are going West on 60." Beth looked at Alex, "Did you program the system? Where are we headed?" A shrug of his shoulders answered that question. "What in the hell is going on?" The car started by itself and backed out of the store parking lot unaided by Alex.

The car took off down 20th Street, turned left at the first cross road it came to, and then swung right on Highway 60, all without human assistance. Alex tried turning the wheel and stepped on the brake, but nothing happened. The car was driving itself. He told Beth they should get out at the next stop sign, but the doors were locked and would not open.

They sped down 60, within the speed limit but weaving in and out of traffic. It was scary. Siri's voice reassured them that everything was ok. Alex was not convinced but couldn't do anything about it. Beth tried to call 911 but phone service was blocked. They couldn't figure out who had gotten control of car, and of them in the process.

After a long ride west on 60, Beth told Siri that she had to go to the bathroom. The car stopped at a service station at Hee Haw Junction. Beth got out and went inside. She had her iPhone with her, and Alex could see her making a call. She came to the car and said she would not get in again. The car drove away with Alex inside.

The police found the vehicle in a parking lot in Lake Wales. That was five years ago, and Beth has not heard from Alex since.

64. A Matter of Perspective

I lay on a rocky ledge high above the village with the valley far below. Looking through binoculars, I could see figures moving around on the street and children playing in a small park. I had been watching the village for several days, trying to decide if it was safe to venture down. I still had some food and water remaining in my backpack, but it would not last long. I needed to make a decision soon. I will not bother you now about how I came to be in this situation, and I will only say that I am in a foreign and sometimes unfriendly country.

Looking though my binoculars again I saw a huge man walking through the village. People were running away from him, clearly frightened. He was a giant compared to the villagers. He was dressed in hiking clothes and carried a walking stick which he used to push away any of the villagers who came too close. He did not appear to be a friendly giant, stomping his feet and swinging his stick aggressively.

I watch the scene for a while as some of the folks brought him what appeared to be baskets of food and perhaps a bottle or two of wine. The giant picked up these offerings and strode out of town. After he had gone, a group gathered in the town square, seemingly engaged in heated discussion, probably trying to figure out what to do about this threatening figure if he returned.

Putting down my binoculars, I pondered my situation. I did not really want to meet up with this giant, but I needed rations and could not remain where I was. I began my descent into the valley and to the village below. I had decided that perhaps I could be the hero who rescued the townspeople from the giant. I did have my gun and was quite capable of using it. Maybe I could intimidate the giant and make him leave for good. I began to imagine what an important figure I could be if I was able to get rid of the giant.

As I approached the village, several things began to puzzle me. First, the road that I had seen from the ledge high above was much smaller when I walked on it; in fact, it seemed more like a path. And what I thought were the outskirts of the village, I was amazed to see were several small buildings and houses. They were about a quarter of the normal size.

I slowed down, trying to understand what was going on. I decided to keep out of sight, at least until I had a plan. I found a place where I could observe the village and not be seen. I waited patiently and soon saw several people crossing the street. At first, I thought I was watching a group of children, but then I realized that they were adults—small adults, probably not more than three feet tall.

From the cliff above the village, I assumed that the people were of normal size and the figure I saw enter the village was a giant. I had gotten it all wrong; a trick of perspective based on faulty assumptions.

I recalled the story of Gulliver and the Lilliputians. I did not want to be attacked by a group of angry, albeit diminutive, villagers. I decided the wisest thing I could do was to make a strategic retreat and leave the sleepy town behind. Perhaps I could find the "giant" and join forces with him, that is if he was friendly.

65. The Obituary

The following obituary was published in a local Florida paper on June 21, 2014:

Roswell Jameston died peacefully yesterday at the age of 73 surrounded by followers dressed in space costumes. Roswell was preceded in death by his mother and father, who in the late 1930s claimed they had been kidnapped by space aliens and taken back to a distant planet where Roswell was conceived and born. The Jamestons had disappeared from their isolated home in New Mexico about a year before Roswell's birth. There was speculation that the plan was hatched to distract from the fact that the expectant couple was not married.

Although many questioned the story, Roswell had no doubts and became the leader of a "religious group" that believed there was intelligent life in outer space. He had an aura about him that was enhanced by his physical appearance, slightly pointed ears and eyes that seemed to have a purple hue. He made a fortune writing books about the circumstances of his birth and his belief that there was life among the stars. His major regret was that he had been too young to remember his space adventure.

In a biography of his parents, Roswell described their kidnapping by space aliens. Of course, the details had been provided through family stories as he grew up, including a description of the space vehicle and the appearance of the aliens. The sheer conviction of the couple helped to make the tale quite persuasive and many were convinced that it had occurred just as described.

Roswell believed that when he died, the aliens would return to earth and take him home. His followers maintained a vigil around the funeral parlor following his death in anticipation of the space ship that would transport Roswell back to the planet of his birth.

Item in local Florida paper the following day on June 22, 2014:

Last night, there was an unexplained series of events at the Maybell Funeral Home in this small coastal Florida town. A large crowd had gathered around the building waiting to see if Roswell Jameston's prediction was true. Would space aliens retrieve his body and return it to the planet where he was born? At about midnight, all the lights in the funeral home and the surrounding neighborhood went off. Some in the crowd then described a sudden bright, blinding light. The crowd gasped, and that was followed by absolute silence. After half an hour, the lights came back on. The crowd forced their way into the funeral home and entered the room where Roswell's body had been placed for the viewing. The body was gone!

Newspaper story in Roswell, New Mexico Space News, June 23, 2014
Last night, vandals broke into the mausoleum of Mr. and Mrs. Jameston at the Roswell Space Cemetery, opened the stone coffins and removed both bodies. Neighbors near the cemetery reported hearing a loud whirring sound sometime after midnight, and a couple of people returning from a night of drinking recall seeing strange lights in the sky. Police are following up on the crime but have no suspects.

Space News Watch, 24 June 2014
The group that regularly reports on space launches, including classified satellite missions, stated today that an unidentified liftoff occurred at exactly 0200 from the general area of Roswell, NM. There is no rocket launch site in the area, but the group suspects that a U.S. government secret surveillance program is the most likely explanation. NASA and the National Reconnaissance Office (NRO) would not comment on the matter.

66. Appetizer, Main Course, and Dessert

I was standing at the edge of the surf listening to the howling wind and looking out at a darkening sky and ominous waves, and then I saw it. A body was floating aimlessly, roiling heavily in the surf as it was tossed closer to the shore. I watched with an intensity that bordered on obsession. My intense hunger and unquenched thirst were temporarily forgotten as I waded into the surf, the cold water splashing around my bare legs. I knew what had to be done.

I could smell and taste the salt as I reached down and grabbed the slippery form, pulling it to the sand. Making my way back to the others in the crudely built lean-to, I knew this meant our lives had been spared, at least for now.

We had been marooned on the bare and stony island for several weeks without any hopes of food or drinking water. We were desperate. You can't blame us. Sooner or later one of us would have to be sacrificed.

PART IV
CACHE

Every writer worth his or her salt has a collection of valuable notes, stories, pictures and observations. For example, I have my son's painting of me and a giant rabbit in my office for inspiration. A true story about surprising my stepmother, another involving Russian writers, forgetting a password, and adopting a dog are all grist for the mill.

67. Pooka

According to *Webster's Dictionary*, a "pooka" appears here and there, sometimes mischievous and sometimes helpful. I have always believed there were large animals lurking around that could be seen if you really believed in them. My Celtic ancestors were believers but saw them primarily as evil.

I remember watching the movie *Harvey* with James Stewart and immediately becoming fascinated with the idea of a 6-foot-plus rabbit. A companion to talk to, a friend in times of stress. How great would that be? You might be surprised to know that I in fact have held an elevator door for an extra moment and then commented that I was waiting for Harvey. Most people never got it. I would name my pooka "Harvey." Not at all original but somehow comforting.

Although I am not working anymore, I could imagine taking him to my old job at the CIA. Of course, we would have to be careful going through security, but except for an extra spin of the turnstile, no one would notice him. It would be practically impossible for one of my coworkers to say something to him, but people talk to themselves all the time, don't they?

It would be fun to bring him into the Oval Office and show him around the White House. Maybe he could accompany me to a national security briefing, and we could later discuss what happened. He could even critique my presentation as long as he did it civilly.

Since work is no longer an option, I could bring Harvey as a special guest to my Monday morning writing group. They would not be at all surprised if I introduced them to Harvey. I don't know if he would have the inclination to write something, but I am sure he could recite a Celtic story or two for the group's amusement.

68. Tired of Being Told What to Do

I am tired of being given an assignment every week and then obediently sitting down and writing another inane story. I want to be free to write something other than what is suggested in lesson 1 or lesson 9. Do you think we are merely automatons that have no ideas of our own? And by the way, who is this so-called writing expert anyway?

This week's assignment was to write a story about someone who has a mixture of good and bad traits. No goody two-shoes or purely sinister character, but a typically complex person. Who wants to write about anything typical? Piss on that! Besides, do such people really exist? They certainly don't come to this writing group.

Let me read a story about a normal person:
"George got up every day and immediately went to the toilet. Then he brushed his teeth and examined his flabby jowls in the mirror. He'd make himself a cup of coffee and decide to have either toast or a fried egg. Then he'd spent some time working at his computer, reading his e-mails, and looking at a porn site. Next, he'd read the newspaper and talk with his wife, all the while wishing she looked like Tang, the blonde he'd been ogling online.

He would eat lunch, read some magazines, and take a nap. After a tasteless meal prepared by his wife, he'd watch the evening news on MSNBC, pleased that President Obama was doing so well. He might turn on a basketball game, and then go to bed at ten o'clock. He looked at his partner in bed beside him and again thought of Tang."

So much for normality! I will write what I want! I like characters who are primarily evil. A reader may not recognize the true personality as a story is unfolding, but in the end, it should be clear. I don't want some pudding mixture of good and bad, all wishy-washy. I want complicated outcomes—preferably evil ones. If you want normal, go to Wal-Mart and write about the shoppers.

So, I say: Take your book of writing instruction and put it where the sun doesn't shine.

69. Three Writers in Yalta*

My name is Alexander Ilyich Rostov. I was born in St. Petersburg, but I spent summers with my family at our estate in Nizhny Novgorod. It was called Idlehour, although there were few hours when we were not busy with our tutors or working around the residence.

At 12 years old, I was well-read and already spoke French and German. My life was perfectly ordered. Breakfast, studies, chores, lunch, games, dinner, and evening readings were usually on the exact hour every day, and the schedule seldom varied. It was a pleasant but very predictable life.

One summer day my father, Count Rostov, received a letter from a relative resting at a hotel in Crimea. The letter asked the Count to come to Yalta to discuss some issues about property owned by the two men. It was a considerable trip, but the Count decided that the issues involved required a personal meeting. He also decided to take me with him. I will admit to putting some pressure on my father to let me join.

My father brought his manservant and a footman to carry luggage and help us move about. We left on the train for the almost forty-hour trip. We had a private sitting area and sleeping quarters that was made up each evening. For meals, we went to the dining car. It was a rather elegant affair. We first traveled west to Moscow, and then south to Crimea.

The views through the train window were endlessly fascinating. South of Moscow there were huge forests. I looked eagerly for the sight of wolves or other wild animals, but all I saw were cows and horses on the occasional farms that quickly shot by. Further south, there were large open fields of grain and other crops. My father said this was the breadbasket of Russia and the land of the fierce Cossacks.

After two days and two nights on the train, we finally arrived at the port of Yalta. It was a grand sight overlooking the Black Sea. Hotels ringed the water, and there was a wonderful promenade. Coaches took us to the hotel. It was really a spa with gardens and baths.

My father spent his mornings talking business with the relative who had asked him to come to Crimea. He rested and took to the baths in the afternoon, leaving me to my own devices. I wandered about the hotel watching people and trying to stay invisible so as not get in trouble with the attendants. I found a comfortable spot behind a palm that was close to several people in an animated conversation. They were discussing the three men sitting on a bench across from them. One of them said that the old man with the long beard was Leo Tolstoy. Another chimed in that he had heard there were three famous authors at the spa—Tolstoy, Chekhov, and Gorky. The group agreed that it must be them.

I had read stories written by Tolstoy and Chekhov and had heard my family talk about the radical writings of Gorky. What an opportunity to overhear the conversation of three famous men! I worked my way closer to hear more clearly what was being said without seeming too intrusive. But then they quickly stood up and went their separate ways.

I needed some information on the three writers. I have always been innately curious. I went to the library in the hotel and found a book published by the Russian Association of Writers that provided some background on the three men. I also checked out a book of Chekhov's short stories. That night, I read several of the stories, thinking that if

I was found eavesdropping on them the next day, I would have an excuse; I was reading one of the authors' works.

The association's book had some good information on my three targets. Tolstoy was an old man—72. He had been born into a wealthy aristocratic family. In 1901, he was already famous and with *War and Peace* and *Anna Karenina* published, his reputation as a great novelist well established. His writings arguing against the established church had created problems with the state, and he and his family often retreated to Yalta.

Chekhov was 41 when I saw him. His full name was Anton Pavlovich Chekhov. He went to medical school and always considered medicine his true profession, but he supported his family by writing short stories. He wrote about Russian street life and the middle-class. Many of his tales involved men longing for their love while miserable with their wives. He contracted tuberculosis in his mid-20s. That was one of the reasons he frequented the Yalta spas.

Maxim Gorky's real name was Alexei Maximovich Peshkov, but he began using the pseudonym Gorky when he became a journalist. Gorky means "bitter," and he was. Gorky was born in the same town where I lived in the summer, Nizhny Novgorod. His first book was written in 1898, and he was a prolific journalist writing about the lower class and people on the margins of society. When I saw him at Yalta in 1901, he was well known as a radical. Gorky had been arrested many times for his writing and was briefly imprisoned.

The biographies did not do a good job describing the three authors. Count Tolstoy looked like a genuine prophet with long, stringy hair and a beard. I had seen pictures of Indian holy men, and he looked just like them. Chekhov reminded me of a physician with his neatly cut beard and round glasses. Gorky had the appearance of a thug; an American gangster.

I asked my father if he could arrange for the hotel photographer to take a picture of the three the next day. At first, he thought it a silly idea but then decided that he also would like a picture of them as well.

The next day, I set out to find the gentlemen. I knew they would likely be sitting in the garden of the hotel in an isolated spot where they thought they would not be overheard. But they had not figured on such a resourceful young spy. I found them easily in mid-morning, drinking coffee and tea, munching on croissants. I positioned myself behind some bushes and waited patiently for them to speak.

Tolstoy started off with an interesting statement directed at Gorky. "You are a strange creature, exactly as if you were born grown up." Gorky responded with some murmured comment but clearly did not want to pursue the thought. Tolstoy, in what I came to recognize as his style of conversation, then asked one of the many questions he posed to Gorky. "Why don't you believe in God?" He then answered his own question. "You don't because of stubbornness; you have been hurt. The world is not what you would like it to be."

Gorky did not respond. I had the feeling that he was often irritated by Tolstoy's direct questions. The three would endlessly debate issues. Chekov generally said little.

Gorky said that Tolstoy loved Chekhov "like the love of an old maid for a parrot, a pug dog, or a tomcat." The three authors seldom talked about their own writings; most of their conversations were about other authors. At one point, Tolstoy compared *War and Peace* to Homer's *Iliad*; one of the few references he made to his own work. They all criticized and praised a wide range of authors, primarily Russians.

Such different personalities. Tolstoy raged against life but was constantly worried about death. He did not trust the instincts of the citizen, either the peasantry or the aristocracy. He wanted to sacrifice himself for a great cause but said he was "unwilling to commit himself to anything larger than himself." He loved the simplicity of the peasants but was disgusted by their behavior. He could not tolerate the Russian church or organized religion.

Dr. Chekov stayed inside himself, diagnosing others and offering clear comments without ever giving a glimpse of his inner self. He spent his life as a practicing doctor and often provided his services for free to those who could not pay. He probably understood the frailties of the middle class better than any Russian writer. Tolstoy said Chekov could have been a better writer if he had stopped practicing medicine.

Gorky seemed angry and impatient with Tolstoy, but clearly admired him. He agonized over injustice and railed against authority, overflowing with anger and frustration. He also expressed some embarrassment about the way Tolstoy expressed his feelings about women; using very crude language I had only heard coming from the peasants at Idlehour.

Chekhov noticed me sitting behind the palms and called out, "What are you doing spying on us? Listening to our conversations?" I stuttered a bit and then said I had been reading stories written by Dr. Chekhov and just wanted to hear what they were discussing. Chekhov asked what story I had read. I said the one about the lady and the dog. He laughed and then asked what I thought of it. In a moment of frankness, I said, "I thought it was a bit tedious." The three of them laughed loudly and Dr. Chekhov gave me 5 kopeks and told me to run along.

Thinking back over my experience in Yalta, I realize that I did not fully understand the conversations I overheard, but I knew the three of them thought and felt deeply about life. I had the impression they were searching for answers to questions that had no answers. Maybe growing up does not help. Perhaps it just brings the unexplainable into focus.

I went back to Idlehour with my father after a week at the spa. I was only 12, but I had matured in ways that could not be easily explained.

The main character in Amor Towles' book A Gentleman in Moscow *was appropriated for this story. The dialogue is from the artists' memoirs.*

70. What Is In a Name?

John Jacob Jingleheimer Schmidt died screaming at his family early in the morning of March 20. I refer to him as John Jacob for the sake of brevity. John Jacob did not go quietly into the night. He passed away ranting at the unfairness of life and his disappointment with his wife, children, grandchildren, and humanity in general.

John Jacob was born on a stormy January night in 1925 on a two-mast sailboat fighting its way across the Atlantic *en route* to Canada. He came into this life the way he left it—screaming at the top of his lungs. His mother, Jingleheimer Schmidt, was the only woman captain sailing the Atlantic at the time. His father, John Jacob Schmidt, was a witless seaman who had found his way to the captain's bunk on a previous voyage. The ship was bringing in illegal scotch during prohibition.

John Jacob inherited a small fortune from his grandfather and never worked a day in his long and somewhat useless life. He went to Yale and graduated without honors. As a man about town, he became famous as a practical joker. He and friends once erected barricades across part of Broadway in New York City. They were thought to protect workers from motorists as they repaired the street but after several days, someone realized there were no workers and thus no repairs, just traffic problems.

He and some fellow pranksters also went into the Biltmore Hotel and told the manager they had been sent to change the light bulbs. They moved every bulb on the ground floor but did not replace a one. That evening when the staff wanted to turn on the lights, nothing happened. The hotel remained dark for several hours until new bulbs were procured. People got to know him well for his pranks and whenever he went out, people always shouted, "John Jacob Jingleheimer Schmidt, what are you up to?" Often, they would repeat it over and over again, slowly reducing the volume.

John Jacob moved to Vero Beach, Florida, in the early 1940s. He did not take up golf, which he believed was a walk spoiled. Nor did he play tennis, which he thought was less manly. He just became a genuine crank, a curmudgeon of the first order. He had several pet peeves. For example, it upset him when people tried to sneak more than 10 items through the fast checkout. He would make a big fuss about counting the number of items. He also disliked seeing people sample the fruit before they made a purchase. Once, he called the manager when a little old lady tasted a strawberry. Driving infractions infuriated him: not signaling when making a turn, veering into the right lane after making a left signal, tailgating... there was no end to his irritation over the slightest driving error.

A crowd gathered around John Jacob's house one evening. They began chanting "John Jacob Jingle Irish Schmidt." They kept it up and the fact that they got the chant wrong so irritated John Jacob that he opened his window and cried out, "It's *Jingleheimer*, dumb heads—"

Then he collapsed and died.

71. The Other Side

I just don't buy it. It sounds so perfect, so peaceful, and helps to assuage the fear of death. And it *does* solve that unexplainable concept of our souls just disappearing without a trace. But the idea of all these millions of spirits milling around, bumping into each other, carrying the same emotional baggage in the spirit world as they did in life is just unfathomable.

Does everyone pass through to the other side or is there some kind of filter; a selection process? Is it based on good deeds, good looks, good intentions, or is it more random? Who writes the rules and enforces them?

Spiritualism is just one of 4,200 religions. Most promise some type of afterlife. All deal with universal human issues, and often try to ease the fear of death that typically increases as we age. It is all very confusing.

Typically, people adopt the predominant religion of their country, or that of their tribe or their immediate family. That means that there is relatively little free choice involved.

Would our lives be profoundly different if we were presented with all the religious options with no expectations? Would our lives be happier? More fulfilling? And if we were happier, would the idea of an afterlife even be necessary?

72. An Epiphany

I have always been a bit crazy, but it keeps me from going insane. For most of my life, I operated just on the outside edge of the law—minor breaking and entering, rolling a drunk, lifting something from a store, and occasionally a bit of fraud. The most serious crime was to fleece a homeowner by promising to do repairs, getting a bit of money up front, and then never following through. I always figured that I was not really harming anyone all that much, just getting what I was owed. I did not consider myself evil, just a bit bent, a no-good-nik. But then I ran into a situation that changed my life.

I had borrowed some money from a couple of toughs. Initially, I had a few weeks to pay them back at 50 percent interest, but I had been avoiding them and was well beyond the payoff deadline. I was in Rossie's Bar on Route 1 having a beer when they came in looking for me. I gave an excuse for being late in paying, but they were not interested. I made my way to the restroom and ducked out through the kitchen.

I ran across the highway, only to cross directly in front of a speeding Volkswagen Beetle. Fortunately, I went right over the car and ended up sitting on the road just behind the bright yellow Bug. I was a bit groggy and surprised that the person who got out of the car looked exactly like Jesus. With long hair and a white pullover shirt, he even had a slightly swarthy look.

He walked over to me, put his hand on my shoulder, and said I would be all right, but I had to change my life. I could clearly hear the words of a country song: "Drop kick me, Jesus, through the goal post of life." I closed my eyes for a moment and when I opened them, I was still in the road but there was no sign of the man or the car, although the song still rang in my head.

My life changed at that moment. I did not start going to church; I did not need to. From the moment Jesus put his hand on my shoulder, I knew what to do and what not to do. I did not need clarification about right and wrong. I can still see him getting out of that rusty old yellow Volkswagen with the bumper sticker that read: "Jesus is coming, look busy."

73. Bus Depot

We were on Highway 99 heading away from Redding, California. I was sitting in a large, overstuffed chair in the back of an old pickup truck surrounded by all our possessions. My mother and stepfather had lost their jobs at the shipyard in Long Beach, California, and after spending several weeks with my mother's friend, we were heading to Seaside, Oregon.

Suddenly there was a bump, a loud screeching of metal, and the smell of burnt rubber. I watched the right rear wheel of the truck roll across the highway as we sat perfectly still.

I am sure Mother's friend was really happy to see us return. The truck needed to be repaired, and it was decided that I would be sent to live with my father until the family got settled. He had remarried a couple of years earlier, and my brother lived with him and the new wife in Oregon.

A few days later, my mother and stepfather took me to the bus depot and I was put on a Greyhound, given a couple of dollars, and sent on my journey to Reedsport, a small lumber town in Oregon. MapQuest shows the trip to be just more than 300 miles and about five hours, but this was 1946 before the new highway, and the Greyhound stopped at every town and road junction between Redding and Reedsport. I do not remember how long it took as I drifted in and out of sleep, but I started in the morning and arrived after dark.

I enjoyed the trip although I do not remember many details. Everyone on the bus smoked, most were friendly, and several made sure I got back on the bus at the various stops, even helping me order lunch—a hamburger and a chocolate milkshake. I have loved the taste of that combination ever since.

I arrived in Reedsport and was greeted by my father. We went home, and I met my stepmother. Nearly 50 years later, she told me that until my mother called to say I was coming, she did not know her husband had two sons.

74. A Hat Trick

When Shirley Temple Black died, it bought back three memories that involved her. When I was five or six years old, my mother went to a Shirley Temple movie and was so excited by the tap dancing that she decided I needed to take lessons. I reluctantly complied, and to my surprise, I enjoyed them. I continued to dance, and in high school, I went to every sock hop and school formal. In the senior yearbook, I was described as the best dancer in the class of 1953.

In 1979, I was made the director of an office in the CIA that produced the President's Daily Brief, a short document describing key events of the day. My deputy was a diminutive and dapper fellow. He was an accomplished analyst who had served as one of the senior intelligence advisers to the Paris peace talks between the U.S. and North Vietnam. Dixon had an interesting background: In grade school, high school, and college, he was an actor in several movies and the voice of a young smart-aleck kid on many radio programs—*Date with Judy, Jack Benny*, and others. When he was quite young, he was a stand-in for Shirley Temple when they were shooting scenes where her face was not shown. He wore dresses and wigs, and they were the same height.

In 1989, I was Deputy Director of the CIA and working with a director who had an enormous range of contacts, including many in show business. I do not remember how he made Shirley Temple's acquaintance, but he invited her out to the Agency for lunch. This was about the time Ms. Temple was appointed Czech ambassador. I did not know he had invited her, or that she was even in the building.

At some point in the late morning, I opened the door connecting my office with that of the director and walked in to find him sitting in a chair next to a small, dark-haired woman. I was introduced to Shirley Temple. I was invited to lunch with them, but after some chit-chat I pulled him aside and said that we had a fellow in the building who had been a stand-in for Shirley. I wanted to invite him to lunch with us. He agreed and during our meal we were treated to a discussion of what it was like to film movies in the 1930s as Shirley Temple and my deputy exchanged stories. One thing I noticed was that sitting in the chair around the dining table, Shirley's feet did not touch the floor.

75. Cleavage

I have always been a voyeur of cleavage. I find it hard to keep my eyes off a woman who has chosen to expose a fair amount of her bosom. Sometimes it can be embarrassing to talk to someone who has presented herself in such a manner. I catch myself not looking into her eyes but much lower.

However, it can go too far. For example, some of the movie stars have chosen to appear on red carpets wearing dresses cut down to their navels. For me that is just too much cleavage. Some modesty is required; after all, carefully presented cleavage is far sexier than total nudity.

I often went to parties attended by an attractive woman who regularly dressed in clothing that revealed a good amount of cleavage. I will admit that I enjoyed watching her up close and from afar. Perhaps I was a little too obvious one evening. She came up me and said, "I have noticed that you have been paying a lot of attention to my chest. I should be flattered but will admit to being a bit irritated by what I consider to be impolite staring." With that comment, she reached inside her dress and exposed a breast. "Now that you can see it clearly, are you satisfied?"

I was speechless for a moment but recovered and said, "It was more interesting before being exposed because there was some mystery involved." At the next few parties we both attended, I made a point of not paying any attention to her cleavage at all, though it continued to be on display.

I had a new idea. If she was irritated before when I just stared at her cleavage, what would she do if focused my attention on the rest of her body?

76. The Cocktail Party Strategy

First, make sure that you do not have pungent breath—avoid the tempting onion and sardine appetizer and a large whiskey. You will be in someone's face throughout the evening. Find that people who likes to talk about themselves and keep them occupied with questions about their fascinating life, their family, and their achievements. Look interested and listen with great interest to their answers.

And while moving very close into their personal space and looking directly into their eyes, take a tiny mouse-step closer and then another and another. They will begin to back up. Move them around the room without touching them. The walk will do them good, and it will amuse you until the end of the evening.

77. One of My Tchotchkes is Missing

Sitting in a comfortable chair in the library, I looked around at the shelves of books and the collection of objects d'art and keepsakes amassed over a lifetime. Wait, something was missing. I did not know what, but I knew that something was out of place.

I began a mental review of what remained, hoping that would allow me to identify the missing object. That led me to study each of the items displayed on the shelves and think about how, when, and where each was acquired. Starting at the top shelf, I began the inventory.

My son Andre's life masks, William Casey's probably the most unusual. I had inherited his limo after his death, and it always felt a little weird to be driven around in it. One evening on a whim, I put the mask on when I was being driven downtown. I always hoped that someone saw me and was startled to see the ghost of Casey driven into the Capitol. My driver did not say a word. He was familiar with unusual behavior.

There was the interesting box, one of several that told amusing stories. This one showed a television with pick in hand in what looks like a pit. Entitled "How TV Works," naturally.

An Andre self-portrait, Andre as a crying baby, the Madonna, two dogs and a black, evil-looking raven I got in Venice. I bought it because it reminded me of the masked ball in Poe's story of the plague in Venice where all of those attending the ball expected to die. They hid what could be a symptom of the plague—a flushed face — behind masks.

Next came the catfish; a fish with the head of a cat. I once had a dogfish, but Andre sold it and I had to give it up. There was another raven, this one done in metal. Sitting to the left was the pig I had on my desk at the Agency. I always wondered what my sophisticated visitors, particularly Muslims, thought of the amusing porker.

I saw the Viking helmet with the horns. And then there was the cast brass model of the fort in the Khyber Pass where a Director of the CIA and I were hosted by the Khyber Rifles. The dinner included a full-grown barbecued sheep placed in the center of the table. You just took your knife and sliced off a piece. The Director, as honored guest, got the tail—it was a fatty-tailed sheep. Also, one of my favorites, the cat fight: A ball of dust with cat paws, tails, and stars coming out.

Pushed to the back there was a harpy I made when Jan was taking a pottery class. And next to it was another Dick Kerr creation in ceramic—a face hanging on the wall with an open mouth in which a plant is supposed to be placed — a "man-eating plant." I was clever in my early days.

I needed to move on to another shelf or I would not complete the inventory. I checked very carefully to make sure one of my favorite objects was on the second shelf. It was a Buddha about 10 inches tall from a frieze in Taxila in northern Pakistan. I was sent to brief the President of Pakistan on the Soviet strategic threat and had a couple days before he could see me. I went to see the deserted ancient city of Taxila that was founded by Alexander the Great during his campaign in Asia. In the city were remains of temples devoted to all the religions of the time. I bought this small statue along the road from a relic hunter who offered to sell me an eight-foot Buddha kept under his bed in a small stone hut. It was truly magnificent, in a toga carved in Greek style, but too large for my luggage. He graciously offered to chop off the head.

There were many other objects in the room that need to be listed. A beautiful, delicate vase given to me by the Greek government during a visit. It has several seals and is clearly Corinthian. Jan says it is not original; she probably is right, but it is a great copy. That reminds me of a comment in a book about Ancient Greece that during the time of Pericles, one of the senators had a factory that made copies of Mycenae art and sold the fakes to Athenians.

There were some extremely valuable books I wanted to make sure were still on the shelf. A couple were the first ones I read as a youngster, and that I had talked about for years. Jan found one online and the other in a used bookstore and gave them to me as a surprise. A Tod Moran book, *The Tattooed Man,* and *Man-Eaters of Kumaon*, a book that my grandfather read to us grandchildren at bedtime. There was a book with several biographies of senior intelligence officials. Only problem was it was in Bulgarian. Oh, there was another truly unique publication, a *Penthouse* magazine in Braille. Think about that. It makes the fingers ache. I bought the magazine at a yard sale in the

Great Falls Town Center. I bought a lettuce box full of smut books at the same sale. I took them to the beach and left them for summer reading by renters, visitors, or whomever. One of the hundred or so books remains on the shelf—a trophy of sorts.

I could not identify what was missing. Maybe all my treasures were in place, but I still had the nagging feeling that something wasn't right, possibly an item had just been rearranged.

Then I remembered the item that I never actually had in hand. During a trip to Istanbul in the 1960s, I had visited the underground bazaar. In it, I found a perfect gift for Jan, a small, ancient—or so the shopkeeper said—statue. I bargained for it over a considerable period and walked away. Then I came back and offered a very low price. The shopkeeper took the statue and put it away, saying he would not sell it to me at any price. I could not believe it. I tried talking him into it but no luck.

My missing treasure is still somewhere in Istanbul, and forever in my memory.

78. The Men's Restroom

She could not wait in the long line outside the women's restroom, so she walked into the men's bathroom. He was seated in one of the stalls when he heard what sounded like the clicking of high heels. He was puzzled and even more so when he heard the door of the stall next to him open and close.

Then he smelled perfume. He looked under the partition and saw red high-heeled shoes. His heart raced, and he felt his pulse. He was confused. Was he in the wrong restroom?

Should he make a break for it before being discovered or wait until he was alone?

79. Kerr Obituary

The Scribblers had a party one evening and each member was instructed to bring an obituary they would like to see used upon their death. I presented the following:

Richard James Kerr, age 93, died yesterday during a meeting of the illustrious writers' group, the Sandfly Scribblers. He leaves behind Janice, his wife of 77 years, four children: Randall, Andre, Kevin, and Meagan, and a host of grandchildren. Mr. Kerr's book of short stories, and his memoir were both number one on the *New York Times* book lists in the fiction and nonfiction categories a few years ago.

Mr. Kerr was a former Deputy Director of the Central Intelligence Agency and served seven years as a commissioner on the group monitoring the Good Friday Agreement in Northern Ireland. He was active in writing articles and speaking about U.S. foreign policy in the Vero Beach area.

Mr. Kerr does not know he is dead and, therefore, has no regrets. His family and friends, however, will miss him.

80. He Passed Away Peacefully

I read the obituaries religiously. I am not sure why. Flippantly, to make sure I am still alive and not among those taken. But really it is to see whether people who passed on are older or younger than I. Have I slipped past the average, or am I just hovering around it?

I realize that the death of someone five years younger than me makes no difference about my own due date, but somehow, I feel better, maybe even relieved that I have outlived them. It is sad that I am more interested in the fact that I am still living than sad about their death. But then again, these are people I don't know.

Several older friends recently died. I felt sad that they were no longer around, but in some cases, they had been quite ill, and invariably I said they were probably better off without the suffering. Also, their loved ones could now get on with their lives.

I may have said that, but I don't believe it for one second. That is all poppycock. How can death be better than living? What is the likelihood that a loving relative is happier alone? Free of a burden perhaps, but left with a void that cannot be filled, an ache that cannot be numbed.

Those obituaries that say "he or she died peacefully" should be burned in a huge fire together with the body of the deceased. Like the India pyres along the Ganges, the flames should consume all and the ashes thrown into the water.

If you think this all sounds like I do not believe in an afterlife, you are right! Heaven and Hell would be too crowded. An estimated 107 billion people have lived on earth. Why should my life be unique except to an infinitesimally small number of family, friends, and acquaintances—clan and kin. The only thing from my life that will have any permanence will be my sons and a daughter, and their sons and daughters, and so forth.

It is difficult to imagine life when you are not part of it. What will happen to all my dreams, my ideas, my thoughts, so brilliant and erudite? Into the Ganges.

81. Packing the Kit Bag

I have had a "successful" life by nearly any measure. But at 80 years old, a happily married wife for 62 years, four wonderful children and nine grandchildren, enough money to live comfortably and much more, I was miserable. I could see a downward spiral of health, no challenges, no victories, just an uneventful and boring future. My life, in the words of Rush Limbaugh, was *caca*.

If I were to disappear, it would not cause a financial burden for my wife. She is very independent. I could use the excuse that I have several days' work in Washington, D.C. I had no excuse for not coming back, but still I began planning my escape.

My wife kept all the financial records, so first I needed to establish my independence. I got my own credit card, cashed some stocks listed in my name only, got a checking account at a new bank, and set up a post office box where my mail could be sent.

I also began collecting some documentation I might need and

making copies of important papers. I realized that I needed many things that I had relied on my wife for: addresses and telephone numbers for friends and children, birthdays, insurance information, and all the other clutter of information necessary for daily life. This process caused me to wonder if "escape" was the right description of what I was doing. Maybe I already was escaping much of life's humdrum problems. But never mind the second thoughts. Things had gone too far to retreat.

I had been fancying, or perhaps better dreaming, of buying a red Porsche convertible and had located one in Vero Beach. I contacted the seller and worked out a price and date when I could pick it up. Things were moving along. I needed a few days to see if I had forgotten any critical things in preparation to begin my new life.

The day had arrived! Independence Day, the beginning of a new and exciting adventure. I kissed my wife goodbye. I will miss her. I wondered if she suspected something was afoot. She usually uncovered my secrets before I was ready to reveal them. I overcame some pangs of regret and loaded my suitcase into the Saab that I was trading for the red Porsche. I had previously put records and some other belongings that I could not bear to leave behind in a small storage site. I drove off with the feeling of high adventure in my future.

Picking up the Porsche only heightened my expectations for a new life. I drove along 60 toward 95, top down, hair blowing in the wind, and wearing a new pair of Porsche sunglasses. I was making my break. It was happening.

I drove past the North 95 entrance and then past the South 95 entrance. Where was I going? I drove for a bit down 60 but then pulled off a short way down the road. After all that preparation, I had no idea where I was headed.

I took off the glasses, put up the top and drove back into town to talk to the dealer who had taken my Saab as a trade-in for the Porsche. I lost money on the deal, but the life lesson was priceless.

82. The Rest of the Story

An obituary in a local news was unusual. It was headlined "Be good to your children; remember, they will write your obituary."

   Kathleen Dehmlow

Kathleen Dehmlow (Schunk) was born on March 19, 1938 to Joseph and Gertrude Schunk of Wabasso. She married Dennis Dehmlow at St Anne's in Wabasso in 1957 and had two children, Gina and Jay. In 1962, she became pregnant by her husband's brother Lyle Dehmlow and moved to California. She abandoned her children, Gina and Jay, who were raised by her parents, Mr. and Mrs. Joseph Schunk, in Clements. She passed away on May 31, 2018, in Springfield, and will now face judgement. She will not be missed by Gina and Jay, and they understand that this world is a better place without her.

Gina and Jay obviously hold long-standing feelings about their mother. But what if there was some reasonable explanation for her actions more than 50 years ago?

Kathleen was 24 when she had an affair with Lyle. He was a handsome young man who had been in several Hollywood movies. She had married at 18 and had two children, and her husband was an uninteresting older man. Lyle brought a spark into her life, and she decided to take it. Off she went to California. Besides, as it turned out, her husband found another woman a year later and also abandoned the children. Noticeably, he was not mention by name in the obituary.

Once in California, Kathleen tried to keep in touch with Gina and Jay, but all her letters were returned. The grandparents had totally cut off contact. She started a new life and as the years passed, her memories of the children, her parents and her ex-husband became more and more faint. But her guilt remained.

Lyle was quite successful, and he and Kathleen ended up with considerable wealth. Kathleen decided to set up a foundation that had a core purpose of providing support to abandoned children. That effort went on for years and turned into a major success.

The world is a better place because of Kathleen.

83. The Writer as an Artist

I cannot draw even moderately attractive stick figures, but I have some ability to write and create. That leads to the question of the connection between these skills. Can a writer describe things in a way that provides the reader the same sensations, the same emotions, the same "picture" as an artist in a drawing or painting? Can I be Van Gogh the writer?

Of course, there is no way for me to live the same life as Van Gogh, or to have the same experiences. Can I have the same tortured soul? Probably.

Don McLean was able to capture Van Gogh's art in both music and words in his song "Vincent (Starry, Starry Night)" His words in other stanzas convey the pictures of Van Gogh.

Are there ideas, emotions, feelings that can be conveyed only in writing or only in art? Fear—I think the painting "Scream" matches the "Tell-Tale Heart." There certainly is art that causes you to laugh just as much as amusing dialogue does. But it is difficult to describe sunflowers as well as Van Gogh painted them.

The dozen sunflowers crowd into the vase. Some already bloomed past their prime, with seeds turning brown. Others exhibit yellow petals tousled like the hair of a child. The flowers jumbled in the jug-like vase, a few dangling, their faces looking down, others staring upward, waving their petals. The nonchalance of the arrangement is charming. But you know that casualness was calculated, arranging the blooms in a flash of color—yellow and gold, brown with green stems.

Still, the words do not do justice to the painting. Van Gogh cut off a piece of his ear in frustration and a fit of madness. If I were Van Gogh the writer, I would not cut off my ear. I would write a story where someone else's ear was cut off.

84. The Fruit Stand

The array of fruit at the roadside stand seemed a bit erotic; a couple of peaches covered with soft fuzz, the red strawberries that reminded me of lipstick, and the vegetables, oh yes, the vegetables. Remember, it was a bite from that sweet forbidden apple that started it all. It was a wonderful X-rated scene.

85. The End of Conversation

Everyone knew it was going to happen; as night follows the day and as certain as death and taxes. The trend began in the 1990s with e-mail, and then Twitter and new technology that intensified each year. People communicated nearly everything using electronic devices. Youth were the vanguard and lost the ability to frame a complete sentence.

More and more "conversations" were held on social media. Even people dining at the same table or together at a business meeting used devices to communicate. Like cursive writing, the exchange of information by verbal means became less commonplace. People began to forget big words and their meaning.

At one point, Apple came up with technology placing a small screen on your forehead secured by a band. The screen showed what you were thinking so people could communicate without talking. The device caused considerable problems in social behavior because unwise thoughts often popped on the screen. People did not have the time to consider appropriate answers to questions about how someone looked or if they were really loved. Comments about the appearance of people on the street led to fights and considerable friction. Workers could not hide their feelings toward their bosses. The device lost favor, but the trend away from "normal" conversation continued.

The government, and particularly law enforcement agencies, were enamored with the idea of information being sent wirelessly because it was easier to intercept. Thought policing became common, and the ability to monitor people became easier.

There were a few elements of society that did not conform. Of course, politicians continued to talk, but fell into the habit of using Twitter acronyms such OMG, ICYMI, etc. Some elite groups continued to write and read poetry in secret meetings, and there were even a few writing groups that read their work aloud. But this became the exception and was considered subversive by the government and outsiders.

If you want to comment on this piece, I would prefer you send an e-mail and not raise your concerns verbally.

86. Charity Begins at Home

We were sitting on a grassy knoll along a historic road in Great Falls, Virginia. There were five of us drinking wine and having a wonderful Sunday afternoon.

Our conversation turned to the brochure we had all received the previous day, giving notice that the Catholic Church was sponsoring a fine home tour for charity to include several high-class houses in the area. Cocktails and appetizers would be served at one residence, and the host would give guests a tour of the 14,000-square-foot abode complete with indoor pool and greenhouse. A fine gourmet dinner would be served at another home with a music presentation by a well-known pianist. The third house would feature an assortment of desserts prepared by a local chef, along with a showing of paintings and sculptures that had been collected throughout the world. Door prizes would include a dinner for four, tickets to the Kennedy Center, and one surprise gift. Vintage wine was to be served at each stop. The cost of the Greater Great Falls House Tour was $100.

The hoi polloi seated on the grassy knoll decided immediately that this house tour sounded a bit too pretentious and over the top. We needed some response to puncture the balloon. The idea of a "Great Falls Lesser Home Tour" was hatched, and preparations began.

The group decided to open their houses for the tour and invite all their "lower-class" friends. The format followed that of the Church tour, and we also developed a brochure. At the first house on the tour, we served saltine crackers with Cheez Whiz and Vienna sausages. That house featured a display of garden tools, many of them broken and rusty. The second house served navy beans and cornbread, and the attraction was a collection of dust bunnies and a large basket of single socks. At the third and final house, the dessert was Moon Pies and Jell-O with marshmallows and a display of half-finished crafts.

Ripple wine was served at all the houses. The cost listed in the tour brochure was $1.24. To add a little mystery to the event, people were told to assemble in a local church parking lot where they would be picked up and transported. We also indicated that there was a "mystery" house included on the tour. There would be door prizes—a check of tire pressure and free air from a local gas station, two gallons of gas from Buck's Country Store, and a single plant from a local nursery.

An interesting aspect of the tour was how many people came not knowing what this was all about or where they were going. At one point late in the evening, one guest asked if the "mystery" house was her house and after being reassured that there was no "mystery" house, she called her mother and told her that she could go to bed because no one would be coming for a visit.

87. Password to Heaven

He sat there with a dazed look on his face. He had forgotten his password; the one he needed to get into Heaven. And he needed it now, because he had been told the previous day that he had only a short time to live.

He had looked everywhere for the little green spiral notebook in which he had always recorded passwords but could not find the one he needed.

What would happen? He did not remember the password for Hell either. He could imagine his soul whirling around in the ether.

He tried the variety of combinations that he had used over the years. Most involved the name of a dog combined with the year he was married. But some referred to the Outer Banks or his CIA background. He should have put it in a special place. Why couldn't he have just committed it to memory? After all, he knew the dates of the Opium Wars in China. Wasn't going to Heaven more important than that?

One problem was that after trying different passwords, his computer sent him a note that because of multiple attempts in error, the computer would shut down for a specific period of time. That only left him more frustrated and more error-prone.

My God, this was no laughing matter.

88. Short and Sweet

They buried him up to his neck, facing the sun in the eastern desert, not realizing that he was going to have the last laugh because he had put on a coat of SPF-60 that morning to protect himself from getting skin cancer, the most common form.

* * *

Looking around the poker table, I realized that each of his eyes was a different color and thought to myself, "Can I kill a man whose eyes remind me of a Husky or should I just shoot him for cheating at cards without all this introspective thinking?"

* * *

He had thick skin and was very strong, but he had been bullied most of his life. They often teased him, sometimes even hit him with sticks and shouted without ever thinking of his feelings. Then one day after more than 20 years of abuse, he lost it, ran amok and got revenge on all those who had treated him badly, stomping them to nothing—elephants have long memories.

* * *

The doctors, nurses and even his parents did not see the small tattoo on the heel of his tiny foot when he was born. It was only after his death many years later that the embalmer noticed that the date on his heel matched the one on his death certificate—it was an expiration date not unlike that on a milk container.

* * *

He sat in his leather chair looking at the smiling Madonna, the cat fish, the mask of Bill Casey, the large nose with hair coming out the nostrils, and the pig that sat on his desk at the CIA and wondered if all this raised questions about his mental condition or if it could be explained by the fact that he had a crazy artist son.

* * *

Sugar was the name of his lover, oh the kisses like ambrosia, the sweet smell of exotic perfume on her neck, her breasts like Georgia peaches with their ripe taste and sweet smell. He would have to be careful; after all, he was a diabetic.

* * *

She was voluptuous, with unusually large breasts, but my advances stopped when she drew the glock 388mm automatic pistol from her bra holster.

* * *

The two of them were as comfortable as a peanut butter and jam sandwich, but not the peanut butter with nuts that so awkwardly sticks to the roof of your mouth, nor the jam that has been processed without seeds that is nothing like what your grandmother used to make.

* * *

The flat-chested women runners were both angry and disappointed as the buxom blond came abreast of them in the final few meters of the marathon.

* * *

The glitterati at the luminary dance laughed at her formal dress with its neckline covered in cutouts of paper, a mistake made because she had confused decoupage with décolletage.

* * *

He was losing his grip as a hired assassin because he could not remember the details of his jobs. In one contract, he forgot whether it was the wife or the husband who requested his services, and in another he couldn't recall which partner of the failing company was the target. His faulty memory was killing his career.

* * *

Everyone loved her tall, elegant, and rich husband, Richard Torey, but they did not know that even though he was deathly afraid of birds, to be rid of her, he had moved into the old chicken house behind the manor. They would also never guess that she hated him so much that she was driving to the farm store to buy one hundred baby chicks and intended to put pullets in Dick Torey's shed.

* * *

Taken prisoner by Xerxes' forces during the war and forced to haul stones for a new temple while being beaten in the hot sun day after day, I decided to try to decipher the cuneiform graffiti on the wall of my cell in hope of some inspiration from a previous occupant. When at last I could translate the message, to my dismay it said, "Work is its own reward."

* * *

I was sitting at my desk drinking straight bourbon out of a paper cup when the door burst open and she strutted in wearing a dress only slightly larger than the cloth I was using to clean the barrel of my .38 police special.

* * *

Richard Hardwell Jenkins III looked down the sights of his .300 caliber Weatherby rifle at the charging rhino and wondered if it was true that its horn was an aphrodisiac, or if that was just a story his wife made up to encourage him to go hunting while she and the guide stayed back in camp.

* * *

When she walked into my office, I immediately noticed the cotton balls she wore as pasties. They were the same small, fluffy bits of cotton I used to clean my dog's ears, and I wondered if she would bark like Brandy if I tried to clean hers.

* * *

He heard the tumblers of the safe fall into position and figured he had 15 minutes to open the door before anyone could react to the alarm. Tumblers. That reminded him of the group of Russian tumblers he had recently seen on television, and while slowly replaying the entire act in his mind, he did not hear the police enter the room.

89. Why Do I Write?

I write because I am looking for an audience; for the same reason actors act and singers sing. I like to test my ideas on real people. I would prefer applause but would take criticism rather than silence. I like being quoted in the press or mentioned in books and being written up on the internet. I would like to have a bridge named after me or a statue erected or even a pyramid built. I would like to have my name put on a public dump or at the end of a dead-end road. It would be better than nothing. I am vainglorious.

I am also afraid of dying and having my ideas, thoughts, and concerns scattered like dust in the wind. I want something left behind so I will not be forgotten, so people will think I amounted to something. In the movie *On the Waterfront*, Marlin Brando said, "I could have been a contender." I too want to be a contender.

There are 7 billion people in the world today. Since the beginning of "human time" there have been more than 108 billion people. Everyone had a unique personality and a set of unique experiences. Millions were creative and bright, but only a tiny fraction are remembered. For the rest, their accomplishments were important only to immediate family or friends for a couple of generations at best. When I die, I hope to be the 108,000,000,001st person to have lived, but with an asterisk after the one.

Is it so bad to want to be remembered?

About the Author

Living on the West Coast with his mother and stepfather, Richard Kerr went to nearly twenty-five schools before he entered the tenth grade. Shortly after joining the army, he married his eighteen-year-old sweetheart. They are still together sixty-five years later. After three years in the service, he attended the University of Oregon. Not the typical start for someone who became the most senior intelligence officer in the US.

Recruited by the CIA after a year of graduate school, he had some great mentors, a lot of luck and some exciting experiences. Early in his career he went on his first overseas trip to brief the Shah of Iran and the President of Pakistan on the Soviet threat. As the head of the office that wrote the President's Daily Brief, he briefed President-elect Reagan daily between the election and his swearing in as President. He first served as deputy and then director of the Agency element that did world-wide political, economic, and military analysis. He was chosen to be the Deputy Director of CIA when President George H. W. Bush entered office.

After his career in CIA ended in 1992, he continued to work on projects for the intelligence organizations. Just before the Iraq War, he was asked by the Director of CIA and Secretary of Defense to head a group looking at the intelligence provided to policy makers before the war. About the same time, he was asked by the Secretary of State to join a group reporting to the British and Irish governments on the "Good Friday" agreement. The agreement was awash with violence and the parties involved were not acting in good faith. The Independent Monitoring Group spent seven years working to make the treaty a reality.

Moving to Vero Beach in 2010, he has been active in the archaeological dig there, regularly lectures on foreign policy in the local community, writes articles for a local magazine and is involved in a weekly radio talk show.

CPSIA information can be obtained
at www.ICGtesting.com
Printed in the USA
FSHW020435220919
62242FS

9 781950 544004